BRIGHT IDEAS

Maths Activities

npiled by Julia Matthews

D0493366

Published by Scholastic Ltd, Villiers House,
Clarendon Avenue, Leamington Spa,
Warwickshire CV32 5PR

© 1985 Scholastic Ltd
Reprinted 1986, 1987, 1988, 1989, 1990,
1991, 1992, 1993, 1995

Ideas drawn from Scholastic magazines.

Compiled by Julia Matthews
Edited by Philip Steele
Illustrations by Ken Stott

Printed in Great Britain
by Clays Ltd, St Ives plc

All rights reserved. This book is sold subject to the
condition that it shall not, by way of trade or
otherwise, be lent, hired out or otherwise circulated
without the publisher's prior consent in any form of
binding or cover other than that in which it is
published and without a similar condition, including
this condition, being imposed upon the subsequent
purchaser.

No part of this publication may be reproduced,
stored in a retrieval system, or transmitted, in any
form or by any means, electronic, mechanical,
photocopying, recording or otherwise, without the
prior permission of the publisher, except where
photocopying for educational purposes within a
school or other educational establishment is
expressly permitted in the text.

ISBN 0-590-70534-2

Front and back covers: Martyn Chillmaid (photography),
Dave Cox (design).

CONTENTS

4 INTRODUCTION

6 BEGINNING AND END OF TERM
Getting to know you   7
Read all about us   8
Balloon game   8
Find the number   9
Clap your name   10
Picture shapes   10
Pat-a-cake   11
How tall are we?   12
Know your way around   12
Concert party   13
Our shoes   13
Table know-how   14
Spending time   15
Did you miss school?   15

16 MATHS IN A BUTTON BOX
Sizing them up   17
Button charts   18
Greetings!   18
End to end   19
Adders' tricks   20
Button lines   20
Gift buttons   21
Find the square   21
Which colour first?   22
Button casino   23

Number bases   24
Line-up   25
What chance?   25

26 OUT AND ABOUT
Where do we live?   27
What's my number?   28
What did we see?   28
Making a map   29
My way to school   30
Coloured houses   30
The day's log   31
Turning points   32
Which way?   33
How many?   34
Angle checker   34
Making plans   35
Can you find the way?   36
Local guide   36
How many at home?   37
Local history   38
Scale models   38
Networks   39

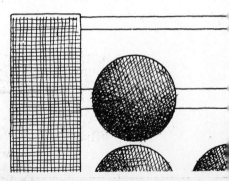

40 FESTIVALS

Easter cards 41
One a penny, two a
  penny... 42
Diwali cards 42
Floating lights 43
Christmas carols 44
Eggs for all 45
Candle lengths 46
Spring flowers 46
Moon calendars 47
Best buys 48
Candle time 48
Diwali boats 49
Note on festivals 49

50 DOMINOES AND CARDS

Sort them out 51
Number stories 51
Lost dominoes 52
Diffy towers 52
Card dominoes 53
How many? 53
Plot-the-dots 54
Dotty dominoes 54
Elevenses 55
Addsnap 55
Domino rectangles 56
Domino chains 56
Fives and threes 57
Target 57

58 TABLE TIME

Lots of twos 59
Bead patterns 60
Blockbusters 61
Number patterns 61
Checking pairs 62
Hurrying home 63
Halt! 64
Who's who? 65
Table check 65
Multibingo 66
Times square 66
Weighing numbers 67
Halve the facts 67

68 PLACE VALUE

Rings and overs 69
Filling the boxes 69
Matchmakers 70
Lotto 71
Cover the numbers 72
High snap 73
Order, order! 74
Making the most of it 75

76 GAMES

Thingamibobs 77
Puss in the tree 78
Clearing the attic 79
Number people 1 80
What's the difference? 81
Hoopla! 81
Shunting about 82
Times snap 83
Number people 2 83
Meeting place 84
It's a goal! 85
Trains 86
Number people 3 87
Mighty magic squares 87

88 PUZZLE IT OUT

O'Grady says... 89
See the queen 89
What-nots 90
Missing 'm's 91
Allsorts 91
Shaping up 92
Right or not right? 93
Sort yourselves out 93
Tell the truth 94
Either... or... 95
Punch cards 96
Square eyes 97
Matchstick puzzle 97
Cows and bulls 98
Thirty-sixers 99
Find the pattern 99

100 MATERIAL TO COPY

126 AN A-Z OF USEFUL MATERIALS

128 ACKNOWLEDGEMENTS

INTRODUCTION

This book is intended as an enrichment to the many existing schemes and guidelines for primary mathematics. It comprises various activities and games which aim to develop basic mathematical skills.

As all children are different, and progress at different rates, it is of course, impossible to state a definite age group to which each activity is geared. The teacher is the best judge of individual pupils' abilities. Nevertheless, each topic covered in this book is presented at three different stages of ability. The appropriate stage is given for each activity. As a rough guide, approximate age ranges are suggested as: Stage 1 – five to seven; Stage 2 – seven to nine; Stage 3 – nine to twelve.

Most of the ideas dealt with in this book are centred on the environment; mathematical topics such as measurement, computation and study of shape will occur naturally. However, there are two areas of mathematics which are well-known as stumbling blocks: place value and tables.

These rate special treatment, and so have sections to themselves.

The sections of the book are as follows:

BEGINNING AND END OF TERM
There is always a possibility that mathematical opportunities might be lost in the more immediate demands of the day, particularly at the beginning and end of term. Nevertheless, *some* mathematics can come out of the first, and last, few hectic days of term. The activities in this section offer some possibilities.

MATHS IN A BUTTON BOX
Few children can resist handling a collection of buttons. For teachers, buttons have a lot of potential for mathematical activities. Start your collection now; you cannot have too many buttons and they are certainly one of the cheapest teaching aids.

OUT AND ABOUT
Children spend a fair proportion of time 'to-ing and fro-ing' between school and home. What do they see? What do they think about? What goes unheeded? The activities in this section will help to focus their minds on some of the mathematics that surrounds them in their everyday lives.

FESTIVALS
Holidays and festivals mark every school year; as well as providing valuable cross-cultural and cross-curricular contact points, they also provide stimulating starting points for mathematics. A few festivals, such as Easter and Diwali, are dealt with in this book, and further festivals are listed at the end of the section. Be sensitive to the cultural backgrounds of your pupils; if you belong to a different culture, ask local community leaders for details of appropriate festival dates and customs.

DOMINOES AND CARDS
Dominoes and playing cards have been with us for centuries, and may be found in many homes. Meeting such familiar material at school can be reassuring for some young children. There are many games which can

be played with dominoes, ranging from simply 'matching the dots' to complicated mathematical structures. There are also many well-known card games; the selection given here has been chosen to give practice in counting, ordering and addition.

TABLE TIME

Most children should certainly have memorised tables by the time they reach secondary school. The important thing is that they should be learnt gradually, in a meaningful and applicable way, so that chanting comes towards the end of primary schooling, and *not* at the beginning.

There is much more to multiplication than meets the eye. Take, for example, the seemingly simple expression 3×2. Does it mean 3 lots of 2 or 2 lots of 3? The answer is *neither* – it is just another way of writing 6. How then does the '$\times$' symbol come in? Take, as an example, two sets of children: The first set has three members (John, Ian and Ahmed); the second set has two members (Ann and Chlöe). The members of the first set can be paired off with the members of the second set (see diagram); the *number* of pairs is the *product* of 3 and 2 and can be written as $3 \times 2 = 6$.

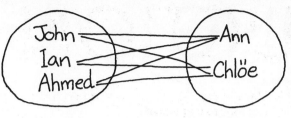

No wonder children often find it difficult to understand multiplication and cannot see immediately that 3×2 is the same as 2×3. Three children with two cards each certainly do not *look* the same as two children with three cards each. Having said this, the *total* number of cards is of course the same, that is $3 \times 2 = 2 \times 3 = 6$. The purpose of this example is to show that the introduction of the symbol '$\times$' should be delayed until the children have had plenty of experience with real objects. The activities in this section should help children towards the understanding and use of multiplication tables.

PLACE VALUE

The idea of place value is confusing to many children. It is a sophisticated shorthand to which, like it or not, they are exposed at an early age. For example, they may live at number 22 and catch a 75 bus to school. The fact that the left-hand 2 is worth more than the right-hand 2 is not immediately apparent; nor is it obvious in any way that 75 means seven tens and five. Plenty of experience is required in the early stages, of the kind suggested in this section.

GAMES

There are countless games produced commercially which are available to schools, and many of them are excellent. The games given here have the advantage that they can be made simply, or the necessary materials can be found in the classroom.

PUZZLE IT OUT

This section contains ideas for 'high-fliers'. They represent an introduction to logic, at each of the three stages of ability.

At the end of the book you will find a selection of material, relating to the activities in the book, which may be photocopied for classroom use without infringement of copyright. There is also a resumé of items that will be useful in class work.

BEGINNING AND END OF TERM

Getting to know you

Stage 1

Objective
An introduction to counting, matching and grouping.

What you need
Large sheets of paper,
scissors,
sticky tape,
paste,
drawing or painting materials,
sticky labels.

What to do
The first few days of term can be difficult for both teacher and pupils. These activities should serve to 'break the ice' whilst at the same time introducing some basic mathematical concepts.

Even in the most informal classrooms, children will at some time of the day be seated around tables, normally in groups of four to six. Each child should draw his or her own portrait, and write their name below it. Explain first that the portraits are to be mounted on a frieze, and discuss a suitable size for them. When they have finished, the children should group the portraits around pictures of the tables, and the whole frieze can then be assembled.

Discussion of the frieze can start off with questions such as: Who sits next to Jane? Who sits opposite Billy? How many children are there round the second table?

How many girls and how many boys are there in our class? How many children are there altogether?

Follow-up
After a week or two, try using the same frieze in conjunction with the class register (always using your discretion if there are any sensitive areas or regular absentees). How many children are absent each day? Write out the figures on labels. The children can select the label for each table and fix it to the appropriate part of the frieze. This can lead on to numerical comparisons between the tables.

Read all about us

Stage 1

Objective
An introduction to awareness of the passage of time.

What you need
Scrapbooks,
drawing materials or cut-out
   pictures,
scissors,
paste.

What to do
In the early part of term a routine is soon established in the class – a daily framework of events. As the children become aware of this, they can begin to discuss the passage of time. This can be started off by each child choosing an appropriate picture and sticking it in a class scrapbook, or by drawing their own picture. The subject might be 'Things we do in the morning' or 'Things we do in the afternoon'. Other books would show what the children do before and after play, or dinner. Individuals might put together smaller books as well, showing what they do before and after school.

Balloon game

Stage 1

Objective
Matching and counting.

What you need
2 sheets of card (A3),
die,
coloured felt-tipped pens.

What to do
On one sheet of card draw the outline of a balloon seller as shown opposite (or paste up a photocopy of page 101). From the other sheet cut out twelve balloon shapes and colour them in: two pink, two red, two green, two blue, two yellow, two white. Make a die with a different one of the colours on each face. Cut twelve small cards and leave them white, with SOLD written across them.

The coloured balloon shapes are placed on the picture, and the 'sold' tags put in a pile on the table. Two players take it in turns to throw the die. They take a balloon picture to match the colour thrown and replace it with a 'sold' tag. If a colour is thrown and both balloons of that colour have already been sold, then the player has to wait for his next turn. At the end of the game, when all the 'sold' tags have been used up, the players count out the number of balloon pictures they have won.

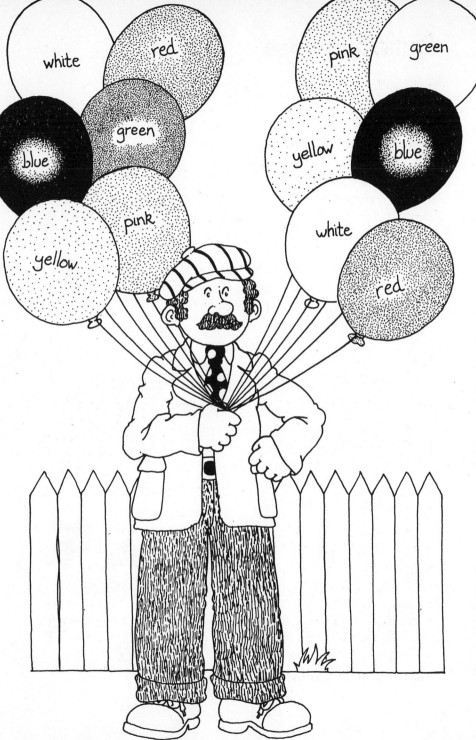

Find the number

Stage 1

Objectives
Matching numbers with symbols; comparisons.

What you need
Pipe-cleaners or chenille stems, large threading beads, 1 sheet of card (A3), felt-tipped pen.

What to do
Cut out nine card labels. Write bold figures (1 to 9) on one side of each, and mark the appropriate number of dots boldly on the other side. Make a hole in each card.

Working in pairs, the children choose a number label and thread that number of beads on to a bent pipe-cleaner or one of the cheap and colourful chenille stems which are available from most craft shops. They then attach the number label as shown. Because the threaded beads are fairly rigid, they can be more easily compared than if they were threaded on laces: Has this one more or less beads than that one?, etc.

9

Clap your name

Stage 1

Objective
Counting and comparisons.

What you need
Large sheet of paper,
felt-tipped pens.

What to do
Each child says his or her first name, and the class then claps the number of syllables: two for 'Ahmed', one for 'Anne', three for 'Jasbinder', four for 'Mrs Watson', etc. The information can be displayed as shown below. Discussion can follow along these lines: How many children are there with two claps? Which set has the most claps? How many claps are there altogether?

Picture shapes

Stage 1

Objectives
Matching shapes; making patterns.

What you need
Die,
gummed paper.

What to do
Cut out shapes from the gummed paper and stick them to the faces of the die: for example, a big triangle, a small triangle, a big square, a small square, a big circle, a small circle. Cut corresponding shapes (scaled up) from the gummed paper. The children work in pairs and take turns in throwing the die. They choose either a large or a small shape to match their throw. After eight throws (or any other predetermined number), they stop and make a picture with their shapes.

Pat-a-cake

Stage 1

Objectives
Cooking for an end-of-term celebration provides many opportunities for mathematical activities. If they were all to be pursued, the fun of making cakes and biscuits would be lost. It is best to concentrate on a limited number of skills, such as balancing, computation and timing.

What you need
Eggs,
flour,
sugar,
fat,
scales,
baking trays,
mixing bowls and
    spoons,
oven,
aprons and oven
    gloves.

What to do
Let a group balance the weight of three eggs with flour, then with sugar, and then with fat. These four ingredients creamed together will make about 24 small cakes. Incidental questions could be asked, such as: How many cakes are in this tray? Are there more in the other tray? How many cakes are there in that row? How many rows are there? How many cakes are there altogether? Will that be enough for us all?

Set the oven at 375°F/190°C or gas mark 5, and cook for 20 minutes (setting the timer, or checking the clock). More questions can follow: What can we do in 20 minutes? Can we clear up before the cakes are ready? Have we time to sing a song, or two or three?

A pictorial recipe could provide an incentive for reading and help future cooks to work independently.

How tall are we?

Objective
Measure and comparison. The teacher should stress the *approximate* nature of measure.

What you need
Measuring
  equipment,
large sheets of paper.

What to do
Working in pairs at the beginning and end of term, the children measure each other's height to the nearest centimetre. After discussion about who is tallest, shortest, or about the same height, the children should record the results on a chart as shown.

At the end of term the children should compare the measurements. Who was tallest at the beginning of term? Who is tallest now? How many children were about the same height as each other at the beginning of term? How many at the end?

Name	beginning of term	end of term
Sharon	105 cm	107 cm
Kevin	97 cm	98 cm

Know your way around

Objective
Routes and plans.

What you need
Paper,
pencils.

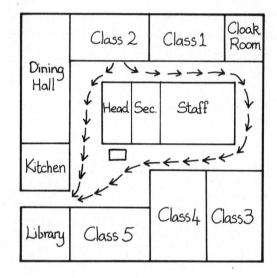

What to do
While children who are new to the school or department are still finding their way around, they can take part in an activity which will help them orientate themselves. How much work is involved will depend upon just how complex the school building is. Let the children discuss the quickest way of reaching, say, the school library from their classroom. Is there only one way? Does it involve disturbing another class or group? Is there a better way, even if it takes longer? Groups of children can then draw out a plan, using arrows to show the routes to various parts of the school – the dining hall, the playground, the hall, etc.

Concert party

Stage 2

Objective
Timing events.

What you need
Stopwatch or timer,
paper for tickets.

What to do
Towards the end of term a concert party might be
arranged by the children. This can involve *timing* (as
opposed to the *passage of time* activities suggested
elsewhere). The children have an allotted time for the
whole concert and must fit in as many turns as time will
allow. Rehearsals will give experience in allowing for
time taken between turns, with the possibility of a longer,
formal interval. There could be much incidental number
work involving the issuing of tickets, putting out chairs, etc.

Our shoes

Stage 2

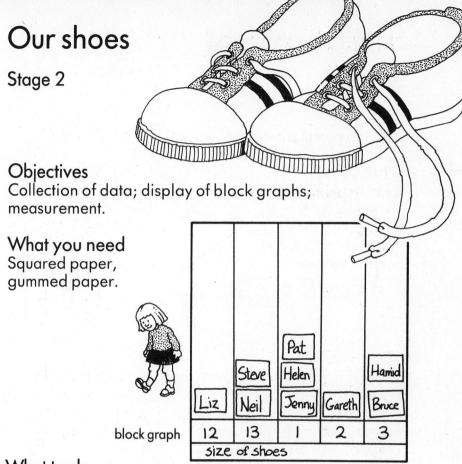

Objectives
Collection of data; display of block graphs;
measurement.

What you need
Squared paper,
gummed paper.

		Pat		
	Steve	Helen		Hamid
Liz	Neil	Jenny	Gareth	Bruce
12	13	1	2	3

block graph

size of shoes

What to do
Here's a starter for the term, based on shoe sizes. There
is no need for measuring, as most children should know
their own size. A simple block graph, using small squares
of gummed paper with the child's name on, can be made
and displayed. The class can then draw the 'shape' of the
graph and record the most common shoe size.
Information could be obtained as to the approximate
linear differences in, say, shoe size 13 and shoe size 1
(both length and width). The children can also compare
this information with the height recordings (page 12).
Is the tallest girl the one with the largest feet?

Table know-how

Stage 3

Objective
Practice in multiplication facts.

What you need
Paper for number
   squares and charts,
thin card for making
   games,
12 cards about
   2.5 cm × 5 cm.

What to do
With a new class you will need to assess the children's multiplication abilities. If there are some children who do

not know their tables thoroughly, games provide useful revision. They enable children who do know their tables to help those who are not quite so confident. All kinds of games may be tried: lotto, snap, filling in number squares, curve stitching. Here is a domino game as an example. Prepare twelve cards as shown:

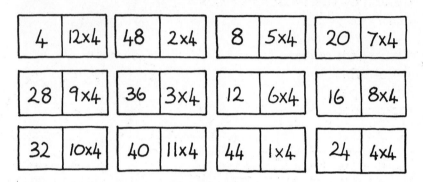

This game is for two players, a 'learner' and a 'checker'. The learner chooses the first domino card to lay down — any one will do, say:

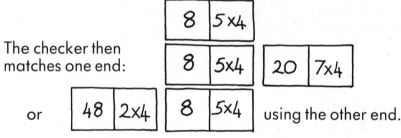

The checker then matches one end: ... or ... using the other end.

They continue to play in turn until all the dominoes are used, the checker making sure the learner is correct and that a complete 'circle' is formed. As confidence grows, a timer could be used in competitions to 'beat the clock'. However, in the beginning it is better for the learner not to feel threatened by a time factor. Cards may be made for other tables as well. To save time, you may like to photocopy the cards on page 102.

Spending time

Stage 3

Objective
Collection of data and ways of displaying it.

What you need
Timetable,
newspapers,
magazines.

Mon	P.E.	Maths	Writing	Nature Study	Reading
Tues	Reading	Art	Maths	Writing	Writing
Wed	Maths	Maths	P.E.	Reading	Writing
Thur	Nature Study	Art	Art	Reading	Reading
Fri	Writing	Maths	Maths	Reading	P.E.

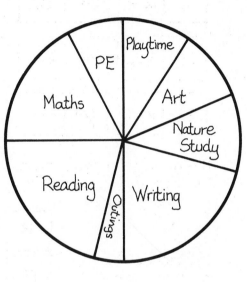

What to do
The beginning or end of term can be a good time to discuss the timetable. How much time is to be spent, or was spent, on the various subjects and activities? What proportion of the total time does each make up? How can this data be presented? Look at block graphs and pie charts. What are the advantages and disadvantages of each method? Encourage the class to bring in newspaper and magazine articles in which proportional data has been displayed pictorially or in other ways, and discuss them.

Did you miss school?

Stage 3

Objectives
Comparisons; computation; percentages.

What you need
Class register,
paper,
pencils.

Name:	Ian	
Week	Days present	Days absent
1	5	0
2	3½	1½
3	4	1
4	5	0
5	5	0
6	2	3
Total	24½	5½
No. of weeks with no absence		3 out of 6

attendance chart

What to do
It has already been suggested that, with discretion, the class register can be used for comparisons in attendance. At the end of term, the days and weeks can be totalled up by each pupil. Some children might be able to express their attendance as a percentage of the total possible. For those unable to attempt this, the number of days present or absent can be compared, and the numbers then used for computation. Figures for the whole class can then be worked out by the children and discussed. The chart shown on page 103 may be photocopied and distributed.

MATHS IN A BUTTON BOX

Sizing them up

Stage 1

Objectives
Sorting; matching; ordering; comparison; counting; concept of 'sameness'.

What you need
As many buttons as possible,
a large button box,
3 smaller boxes.

What to do
The children can enjoy the button box for some time, sorting the buttons and discussing various characteristics such as size, colour, thickness, shininess, number of holes . . . The three smaller boxes can then be introduced, labelled thus:

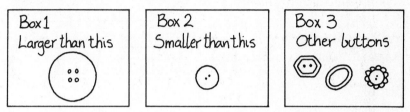

| Box 1 Larger than this | Box 2 Smaller than this | Box 3 Other buttons |

Children work in small groups, sorting the buttons into the appropriate boxes. After an attempt at estimating how many buttons are in each box, the contents can be counted out. How many buttons were there in box 1? How many in boxes 2 and 3? Which box has the most . . . the least . . . the same number?

Button charts

Stage 1

Objective
Comparison of numbers.

What you need
A set of buttons of about the
    same size,
paper,
felt-tipped pens.

we stay for dinner		we go home for dinner	
⊙	⊙	⊙	
⊙	⊙	⊙	
⊙	⊙	⊙	
⊙	⊙	⊙	
⊙		⊙	
⊙			
⊙			
⊙			

What to do
Diagrams can be made showing some simple, child-
centred information. Buttons are used as markers, one to
represent each child in the class. Use various kinds of
charts to find out: Who goes home to dinner?/Who stays
at school? Who prefers cola?/Who prefers orange
squash?, etc. The charts offer a chance to make
numerical comparisons.

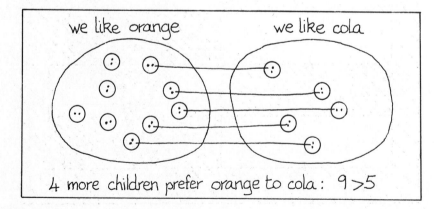

we like orange   we like cola

4 more children prefer orange to cola: 9 > 5

Greetings!

Stage 1

Objective
Comparisons of shape and size.

What you need
Buttons,
thin card,
glue or needles and
    thread,
spray glitter or paint.

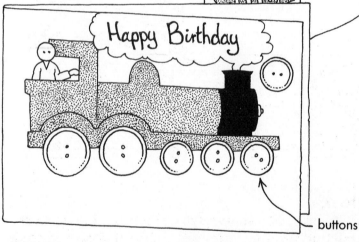

buttons

What to do
Buttons can be used to make greetings cards for all
occasions. The children can glue or sew buttons on to the
cards, discussing their shape and size, and comparing
their other qualities.

End to end

Stage 1

Objective
Strategies and position.

What you need
Sheet of card,
3 buttons of one
   colour,
3 buttons of another
   colour.

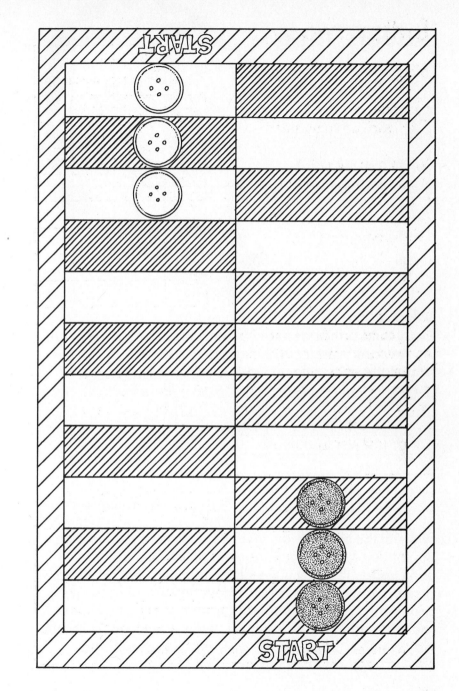

What to do
Mark out a board as shown opposite. The players start
with three buttons each, placed as shown. A turn consists
of one move forwards, or sideways, but *not* backwards.
The opponent's pieces may be captured, as in draughts.
Each player tries to prevent her opponent from reaching
the other end; the winner is the player who can get
the most buttons from one end to the other.

Adders' tricks

Stage 2

Objective
Addition of 'long tots'.

What you need
Plenty of buttons,
paper.

What to do
Each child brings as many buttons to school as they can.
As they are brought in, the numbers are recorded as a
'long tot'.

Name	No. of buttons
Alun	4
Keith	6
Meena	9
Laura	3
Brian	10

'long tot' record

First, let the children discover their own ways of finding
the total number of buttons brought in. Then ask if they
can change the way in which the numbers are grouped in
order to get quick results. Discuss how *you* might vary the
order and suggest combinations of numbers which would
facilitate addition. Remember always that there is no one
way which is 'correct'. The children's own strategies
should be given due consideration.

Button lines

Stage 2

Objectives
Partitions of 10;
conservation of number.

What you need
Buttons,
thread.

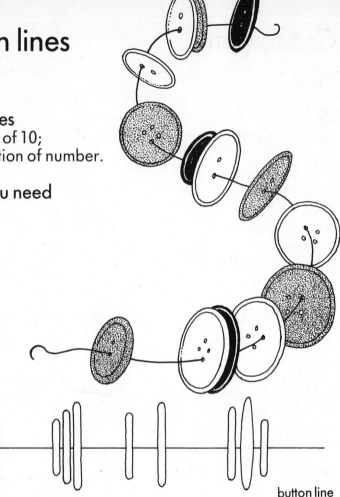

button line

What to do
The children thread ten buttons together to form their
own, individual, moveable number line. By moving the
buttons back and forth, different number combinations
are formed, for example, 5 – 2 – 3. The children then
record as many combinations as they can, and see who
can find the most. There are, in fact, 511 combinations for
10! Here are just a few: 1 – 9; 1 – 1 – 1 – 1 – 6; 5 – 2 – 1 – 1 – 1.

Gift buttons

Stage 2

Objectives
Sorting; symmetry.

What you need
Buttons,
thick card,
safety-pins,
glue or
   needle and thread,
mirror.

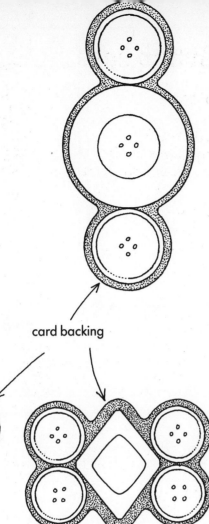

card backing

safety-pin

What to do
The children can make a button brooch for a birthday, Mother's Day or for a Christmas gift. The buttons are stuck or stitched to a piece of card, and a safety-pin is attached to the back. There *is* one rule: the brooch must be symmetrical. This can be checked by placing a mirror across the centre of the brooch. The activity should provide a lead into a discussion of other examples of symmetry.

Find the square

Stage 2

Objective
Sorting two criteria.

What you need
Large sheet of paper,
about 15 buttons.

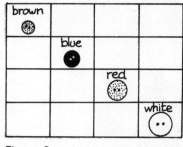

Figure 1

size colour	⊙	⊙	⊙
red			
blue			
brown			
white			

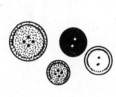

Figure 2

What to do
Draw up a grid as shown in Figure 1 or photocopy the chart on page 104. A child is given perhaps 15 buttons, a dozen of which will fit the categories shown on the grid. When the appropriate buttons have been placed on the grid in the correct squares, ask about the extra buttons, in order to ensure that the activity has been thoroughly understood. The child then records what he has done, in his own way.

Follow-up
A more testing version of this activity would be to prepare a grid as in Figure 2, with no categories shown. You start the sorting process and ask the child if she can guess the categories, and then fill in the rest of the buttons. Finally, ask in how many ways the total number of buttons can be expressed, for example: $4 + 4 + 4 + 4$, or 4×4.

Which colour first?

Stage 2

Objective
First ideas of probability.

What you need
About 16 coloured buttons (for example, 11 white, 4 red, 1 yellow or other colours in similar proportions), opaque bag, paper.

What to do
Working with small groups, get the children to predict which colour of buttons will come out of the bag first, having previously counted the buttons in. Ask the reason for their choice. Then get each child in the group to take out a button in turn, record the colour and then replace it. The class can then build up their own graph by collating each group's information.

Group 1	
White	‖‖‖
Red	‖
Yellow	

Group 2	
White	‖‖‖
Red	‖
Yellow	‖

Group 3	
White	‖
Red	‖‖‖ ... ‖
Yellow	

Which colour came out first?

number	white	red	yellow
19			
18			
17			
16	X		
15	X		
14	X		
13	X		
12	X		
11	X		
10	X		
9	X		
8	X		
7	X		
6	X		
5	X	X	
4	X	X	
3	X	X	
2	X	X	
1	X	X	X

Button casino

Stage 3

Objective
Number bonds.

What you need
Buttons,
card,
pencils,
scissors.

chips

use pencil as central pin

8x2 6x2
11x2 3x2
4x2 5x2
7x2 9x2

card spinner

What to do
Working in groups of two or three, the children can make spinners from card and pencils marking them as shown, in order to reinforce number facts. The buttons are used as 'chips'. The group takes turns with a spinner, and if, for example, 3 × 2 comes up, the player takes six buttons. After five spins each, the buttons are totalled and then arranged so that the totals may be easily checked. They may for instance, be ranged in groups of two, three, five, or ten and so on, as chosen by the children.

Number bases

Stage 3

Objective
Number bases.

What you need
Buttons of 3
  different sizes
  (large, medium,
  small),
die,
paper.

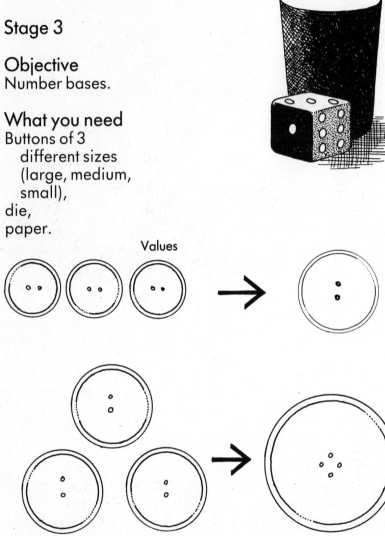

Values

What to do
The players settle beforehand on the number base. Say they choose 3: in this case three small buttons will be traded for one medium button, and three medium for one

large. The players take turns in throwing the die and taking the appropriate number and size of buttons. For example, if 4 is thrown, the player takes one medium and one small button. Each throw is recorded, as the players accumulate their buttons:

Name : Jane				
Throw	die score	large	medium	small
1	4	0	1	1
2	6	0	2	0
3	1	0	0	1
4	2	0	0	2
5	4	0	1	1
6	6	0	2	0

After an agreed number of throws (perhaps six) the buttons are totalled by each player, remembering that three small buttons are replaced by one medium, and three medium by one large:

Name: Jane	Total	large	medium	small
		2	1	2

These totals can be checked against the number of actual buttons, again 'trading up' as necessary. Finally, the scores can be changed into base 10, so that this example would be:
base 3: 212 is base 10: $(2 \times 3^2) + (1 \times 3) + (2 \times 1) = 23$
The players can then suggest their own variations, such as using different bases and throwing two dice.
The score sheet may be photocopied from page 105.

Line-up

Stage 3

Objective
Strategies.

What you need
Thick card,
felt-tipped pens,
2 different coloured
    sets of 10 buttons.

What to do
The children make the board from the card and mark it in
squares as shown. Each player chooses a colour, and
takes it in turn to place one button of that colour on the
board. The object of the game is to prevent the opponent
from completing a line. The lines made may be vertical,
horizontal or diagonal. The first player to get a line is the
winner of that game; a match consists of three games.
Invite the children to make up a similar game, five in a
row, for example, or no diagonals.

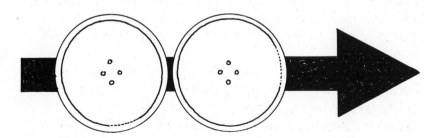

What chance?

Stage 3

Objective
Ideas of
probability.

What you need
About 16 coloured buttons
    (for example, 11 white, 4
    red and 1 yellow or other
    colours in similar
    proportions),
opaque bag,
paper.

What to do
Repeat the activity shown on page 22. At this stage, the
children's explanations may be more explicit. Ask
questions such as: What is the probability of a white
button coming out first? Would the probability be any
different if there were more or less white buttons? What
would the graph be like if the buttons were *not* replaced
each time they were drawn out of the bag? Suggest the
children try the latter.

OUT AND ABOUT

Where do we live?

Stage 1

Objectives
Matching, sorting and counting; comparisons.

What you need
Paper, felt-tipped pens, drawing materials.

What to do
Discuss the houses, flats and shops which can be seen on the way to and from school. Then let the children discuss their own homes and get them to draw a picture of themselves. Each child then signs his picture and puts it into the appropriate set – house, flat, shop – according to where he lives.

We live in a house | We live in a flat | We live over a shop

The same information can also be shown as follows. Which diagram is best for displaying information clearly?

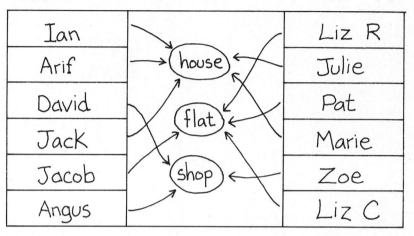

Ian		Liz R
Arif	house	Julie
David		Pat
Jack	flat	Marie
Jacob		Zoe
Angus	shop	Liz C

No	house	flat	shop
6			
5			
4			
3			
2			
1			

Discussion can follow on such topics as: Do more children in our class live in a flat or in a house? How many more? Can we find this out without counting all the pictures? How many children have we counted altogether?

What's my number?

Stage 1

Objective
Ordinal number.

What you need
Sheets of paper,
felt-tipped pens,
pencils.

What to do
Draw a number line (say 1 to 100) with bold figures. Pin it
to the wall. Make a list of all the children's names and the
numbers of the houses where they live. Get each child to
pencil a ring around their own house number on the line.
You can then ask questions such as: Do some of you
share the same number? Are there more rings round the
numbers less than 50 or more than 50? Does anyone live
in a house not shown on our number line (for example,
122, 15a, or 'Mon Repos')? Do we know about odd and
even numbers?

number line

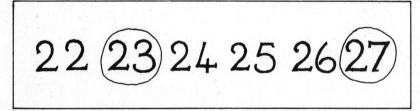

What did we see?

Stage 1

Objective
Spatial
vocabulary.

What you need
Paper and
felt-tipped pens,
or blackboard
and chalk.

What to do
Conventional maps are too abstract to be readily
understood by young children; making picture maps is a
much more meaningful way of recording familiar places.
After a visit to the local playground, draw a very large
circle on paper or on the blackboard, and start class
discussion by saying: 'That's the playground we visited –
what should we have in our picture?' The answers should
come readily, and include such features as swings,
roundabouts, sandpits, slides, litter bins, huts, houses,
cafés . . . These can all be drawn inside the large circle,
after discussing relative positions.

Making a map

Stage 1

Objectives
Ideas of
map-making;
spatial vocabulary.

What you need
Paper,
pencils,
felt-tipped pens,
Plasticine,
kitchen foil,
cocktail sticks,
twigs.

What to do
Choose a small local area that is well-known to the children: it should have a simple and striking layout. The children can help to make a picture map, as on page 28, and mark in any landmarks. This will not, of course, be drawn to any accurate scale, but relative positions should be discussed ('next to', 'between', etc). The teacher then draws out a 'base map', showing the roads, etc as near to scale as possible.

The children can then make Plasticine models of the items on the original picture map, and place them in position on the base map. Informal discussion might be used to tackle the idea of scale; every item should be kept approximately to scale. Small twigs may be cut for 'trees', and cocktail sticks wrapped in foil can make 'lamp-posts'.

twig trees

lamp-post (foil and cocktail stick)

Plasticine bases

Plasticine bridge

base map (paper)

Stirling Avenue

Forfar Road

Kintyre Road

Plasticine building

pond (foil)

High Street

Plasticine wall

My way to school

Stage 1

Objective
Planning routes.

What you need
Paper,
pencils.

What to do
For some children the experience of helping to make a
class picture map could lead on to making a picture map
of their own – the route to and from school, for example.
The children will begin to appreciate that a map helps
you to find your way around: it is not just the shape of a
country, as found in an atlas, but a representation of your
own environment.

Coloured houses

Stage 1

Objective
Spatial ordering.

What you need
Modelling
   materials or
   painting
   equipment and
   paper,
coloured beads,
thread.

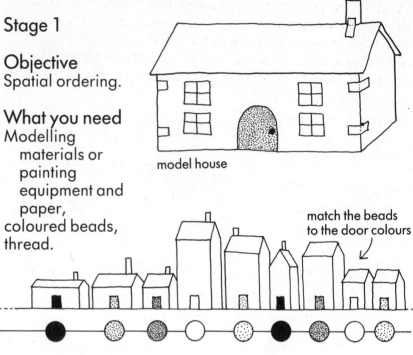

model house

match the beads
to the door colours

What to do
The children should model or paint nine houses with
different coloured front doors. If about five colours are
used, the colours may be repeated (for example, three
green, two red, two yellow, one blue, one brown door).
Discussion should follow on the various shapes of the
houses, their comparative sizes, width, height, etc. Ask
one or two of the children to arrange the houses in a line.
The children should then be given about 20 coloured
beads including about three of each of the front door
colours. They should try to thread the beads in the same
colour sequence as the front doors, whilst the teacher
encourages the use of relevant vocabulary such as 'next
to', 'in between', 'before', 'after', etc.

Follow-up

Put one house picture or model of each colour in a row. Prepare work cards, or use oral instructions, to help individual children reinforce their ideas of 'neighbourhood' and practise some ordinal terms. The kinds of questions that might be asked are shown below.

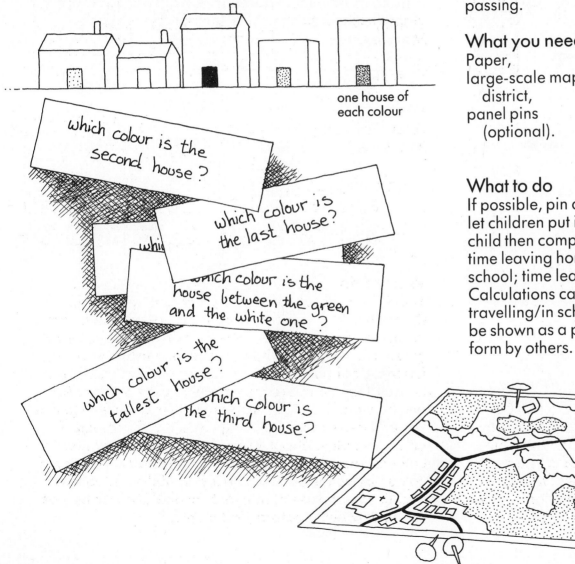

one house of each colour

which colour is the second house?

which colour is the last house?

whi...

which colour is the house between the green and the white one?

which colour is the tallest house?

which colour is the third house?

The day's log

Stage 2

Objective
Notion of time passing.

What you need
Paper,
large-scale map of district,
panel pins (optional).

↑	Anita: How I spent yesterday				
13					
12					
11					
10	▓				
9	▓				
8	▓				
7	▓				
6	▓	▓	▓		
5	▓	▓			
4	▓	▓		▓	
3	▓	▓		▓	
2	▓	▓	▓	▓	▓
1	▓	▓	▓	▓	▓
hours	in bed	at school	travelling	indoors	playing out

block graph

What to do
If possible, pin a large-scale local map on the wall and let children put in pins to represent their homes. Each child then compiles her own 'log' of the day's activities: time leaving home in the morning; time arriving at school; time leaving school; time arriving back home. Calculations can be made of the amount of time spent travelling/in school/at home/in bed. This information can be shown as a pie chart by some children, or in a simpler form by others.

pie chart

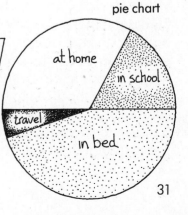

at home

in school

travel

in bed

31

Turning points

Stage 2

Objective
Ideas of angles and turns.

What you need
Compass,
chalk,
sheets of thin card.

Children can take turns in standing on one of the points and responding to instructions such as 'take a complete turn'; 'take a quarter turn'; 'take a half turn'. After each move, the child will call out the point she is now facing. This could be followed up by children making their own compass face on a circle of thin card. The circle is folded into four and then opened out so that the points can be marked in. Individual question and answer cards are used; the children can check their answers with the compass face.

Instructions			Answers
Point facing at start	Turn	Direction of turn	↓
North	Complete	right	North
North	¼	left	West
North	¾	right	West
South	½	right	North.

What to do
Find out if there are any Cubs and Brownies in the class and encourage one or two of them, if possible, to lead a discussion about the points of the compass. Talk about ways of finding out roughly where north, south, east and west are, without using a compass – by observing the sunrise, the sunset, or the Pole Star for example. Next, get a group to draw the points of the compass in the playground, or in the classroom if space will allow.

Which way?

Stage 2

Objective
Developing strategies.

What you need
Sheet of thick card (A3),
felt-tipped pens,
die,
counters.

What to do
This is a shopping game for two players. Prepare a board as shown (or paste up a photocopy of page 106), and give the players a counter each and a die. Starting from SCHOOL on the board, each player throws the die in turn and can move backwards or forwards by the appropriate number of squares each time. The SWEET SHOP and the PAPER SHOP must both be visited (in any order) before going HOME. A player may pass the shop, but it only counts as a proper visit when the counter actually lands on the shop square. The first player to reach HOME, after visiting both shops, is the winner.

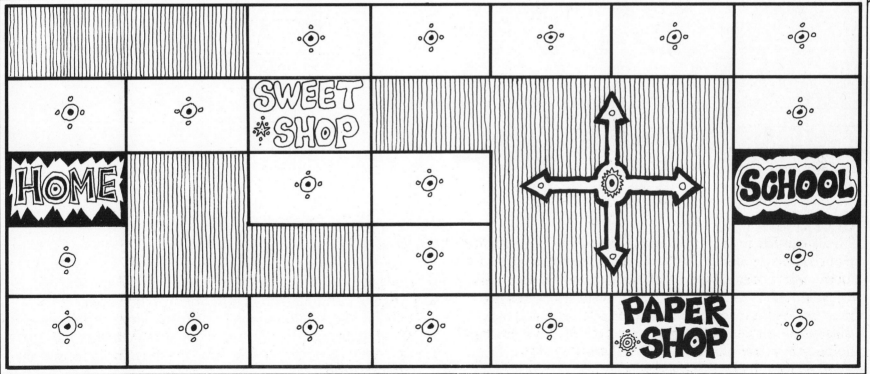

How many?

Stage 2

Objective
Counting.

What you need
Clipboards,
paper,
pencils.

What to do
A walk outside the school may be arranged for small groups, each looking for some particular feature to count, and recording it on their clipboards, for example, cars with only one driver; red cars; prams; and so on . . . Back in the classroom, an open-ended discussion may follow on topics such as: In which direction were most of the people travelling, and why? Will the flow of traffic be reversed later in the day, and why?

Angle checker

Stage 3

Objective
Idea of right angles.

What you need
Pieces of paper,
objects with right-angled
corners.

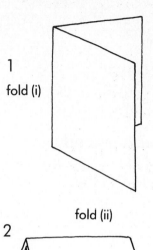

1
fold (i)

fold (ii)

2

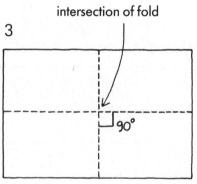

3

intersection of fold

90°

opened out

What to do
The children can make a 'right-angle checker'. All they have to do is take a piece of paper (any shape will do), fold it in half and then in half again. When opened out, the intersection of the folds forms right angles. The sheet of paper can be used to ascertain whether the corners of objects at home or in the classroom form right angles.

Making plans

Stage 3

Objective
Idea of scale drawing.

What you need
Right-angle checker
   (see opposite)
paper,
pencils,
rulers.

What to do
Working in small groups, let the children make plans of different parts of the school – the classroom, hall, library and corridor – using right angles where appropriate. Any cupboards, tables, windows and doors should be drawn in, roughly to scale. Now take turns, within each group, to hide a small object in the classroom, hall, etc. The other groups have to follow instructions and use the plan to find the object. The instructions could include additional information – 'It's about 2.5 cm off the floor', 'Turn left when you enter the room and pass the first cupboard' . . .

school plan (using right angles)

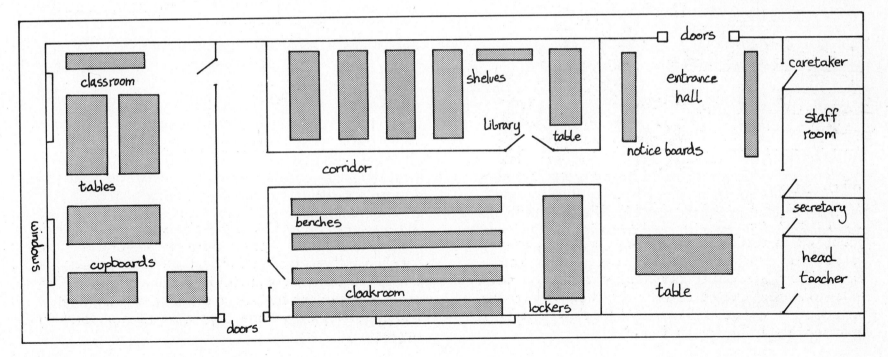

Can you find the way?

Stage 3

Objective
Planning routes.

What you need
Paper,
pencils.

Local guide

Stage 3

Objective
Using grids.

What you need
Paper,
pencils,
street plan (optional).

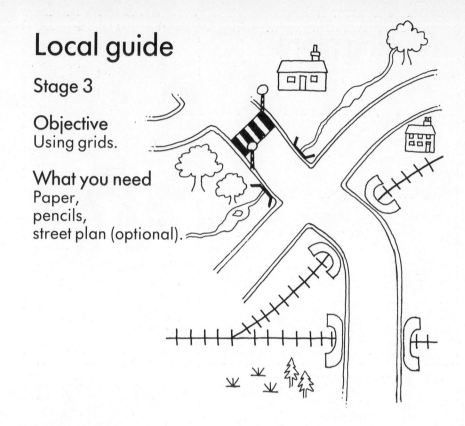

What to do
Working individually or in pairs, get the class to draw their own route home, making it clear enough for an imaginary friend to visit them. Make sure that the children remember to indicate any zebra crossings and features or landmarks such as churches, stations and bus stops which will help their 'friend' to find the way more easily. Discussion should follow on routes which may be longer but safer because of the nature of the roads or traffic. It might be possible to check one or two of the routes when the class makes a local trip.

What to do
The children list the local amenities such as bus stops, railway stations, telephone boxes, public libraries, post offices, places of worship, shops and markets. Some of these amenities can then be shown on a large numbered grid, with the school in the centre (the grid on page 107 may be photocopied). In this way a guide to the town or village can be compiled, with the help of a local street plan.

Questions can then be put on work cards, for example: Where is the nearest police station to the school? Find the nearest telephone box to the school. What building is in square D4? Get the children to make similar work cards for their friends.

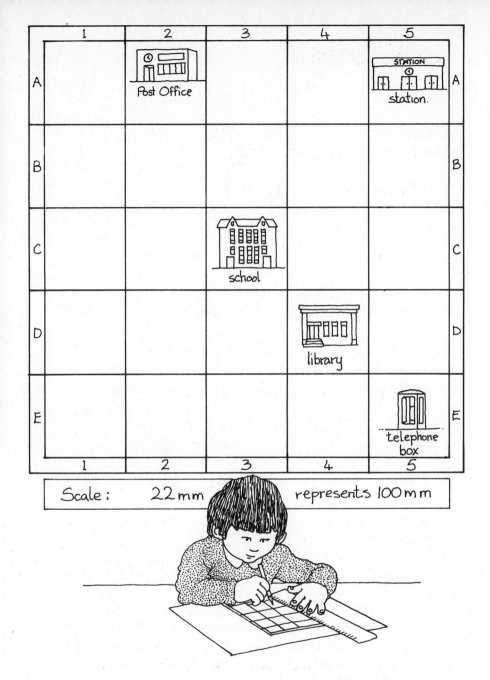

Scale: 22 mm represents 100 mm

How many at home?

Objective
Ways of
displaying data.

What you need
Paper,
pencils,
calculator.

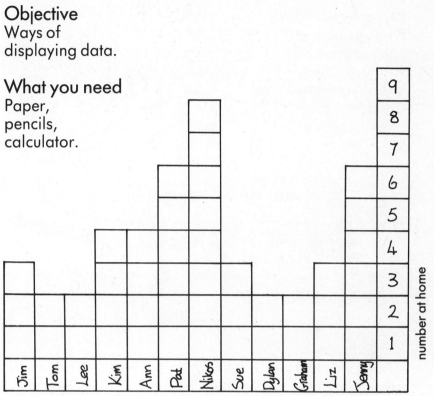

What to do
Find out from each child how many people live in his or
her house. The children then work in small groups and
produce their own ways of displaying the information
collated from the class. The total amount of people
included in the data can be worked out mentally and then
checked with a calculator. Can the children work out the
average number of people to a house? The information
can be displayed on a distribution chart as shown.

Local history

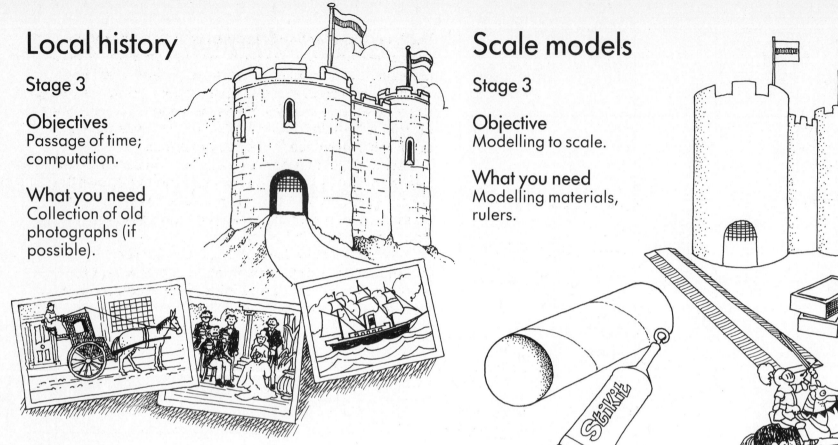

Stage 3

Objectives
Passage of time;
computation.

What you need
Collection of old
photographs (if
possible).

What to do
After a visit to the local library, museum or archive
centre, let groups compile a chronological history of the
district, citing, for example, the oldest building, the oldest
inhabitant, the oldest shop, the date the school was built
and the dates that any important local monuments were
erected. Encourage children to work out the number of
years between, for example, the completion of the oldest
church and the erection of the newest telephone box. The
present population figures can be obtained and
questions asked about them. Have the numbers
increased or decreased in the past ten years? Why? Find
some old photographs and discuss them.

Scale models

Stage 3

Objective
Modelling to scale.

What you need
Modelling materials,
rulers.

What to do
Working in small groups, let the children choose a local
building they would like to model to scale. Approximate
measurements must be made, and the scale determined
through discussion. This will give an idea of 'scaling up'
and 'scaling down' as an introduction to ratio. Modelling
materials might include matchboxes, sweet tubes,
chocolate boxes, foil, etc.

Networks

Stage 3

Objective
Introduction to topology.

What you need
Paper,
pencils.

traversing the network

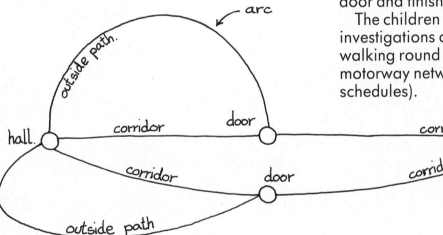

The lines representing the routes which can be taken are called 'arcs' and the blobs where two or more arcs meet are called 'nodes' or 'vertices'. Encourage the children, however, to make up their own words: anything descriptive (and sensible!) such as 'roads', 'paths', 'lines', or 'routes' will do for arc; 'dots', 'points', 'intersections' or 'blobs' will suffice for nodes or vertices.

Deciding whether or not a network can be traversed needs careful thought. The example (below) shows that we cannot traverse the whole network if we start in the classroom or in the hall, but we can if we start at one door and finish at the other.

The children keen enough to go on with such investigations can study examples such as ways of walking round the school, footpaths around a village, motorway networks and air routes (from maps and schedules).

What to do
An introduction to topology can help the children to learn something more about their environment. The problem discussed below is essentially the same as the puzzles which appear in children's books or comics, where you have to draw a diagram without taking your pencil off the paper or going over the same line twice. This is called 'traversing the network'. Here is an example which the children might try for themselves. It shows ways of going from the classroom to the hall.

Note to teachers
Nodes are of two types: those having an even number of converging arcs, and those having an odd number. If there are more than two odd nodes, it will prove impossible to traverse the network. If (as in the illustration above) there are two odd nodes, then the route must start with one and end at the other. If there are no odd nodes, the walk is possible, starting and ending at the same point. The number of even nodes makes no difference. Is it possible to make a network with only *one* odd node?

FESTIVALS

Easter cards

Stage 1

Objectives
Awareness of shape and size; sorting and counting.

What you need
Card or paper, counters or coins, crayons.

What to do
Using a piece of card approximately 20 cm × 15 cm, each child makes a special card to take home or give to a friend. Plain paper will do if card is not available. The example given is to celebrate Easter, but it can be adapted to suit other religious festivals (whether Christian, Judaic, Hindu or Islamic) or secular occasions such as May Day or Hallowe'en.

Class discussion about the shape of the card should precede this activity, and you should demonstrate how the card may be folded in half so the *shape* remains the same although the *size* is smaller. For an Easter card, each child might draw a chick or a rabbit using two counters or coins of different sizes as templates.

Follow-up
Before the cards are taken home, they may be displayed and sorted according to whether there are chicks or rabbits on the front. Alternatively, they could be displayed in a long line and matched to each child's name. This provides a good opportunity for counting: some children might be able to count in twos and threes. Everyone can join in with the counting of small and large circles and the comparison of the results.

One a penny, two a penny . . .

Stage 1

Objectives
Sharing and
computation.

What you need
Hot cross buns.

What to do
As a special treat for end of term, some hot cross buns
can be brought in, or cooked to your own recipe. You will
need about one for every four children. The shape of the
buns and the cross might be remarked upon before the
ceremony of dividing each bun into four. The important
questions arising might be on these lines: What would
happen if we had two more children in the class?
Supposing three children did not want any? If each bun
cost 10p, how much did they cost altogether? How much
did each quarter cost?, etc.

Diwali cards

Stage 1

Objectives
Sorting;
counting.

What you need
Thin card,
coloured paper,
scissors,
paste,
pencils.

candles cut from paper

What to do
Diwali is a festival of light, celebrated by Hindus and
Sikhs. It is a beautiful festival in which candles are lit in
the home. A special Diwali card can be made in class.
Group discussion should precede the activity: How is the
card to be folded, and what is the resulting *size* and
shape? Candle shapes can then be cut from coloured
paper and pasted on to the card, after discussion about
cutting lengths. After the cards have been completed,
with a message inside, and before they are taken home,
they can be displayed and sorted according to the
number of candles on each one.

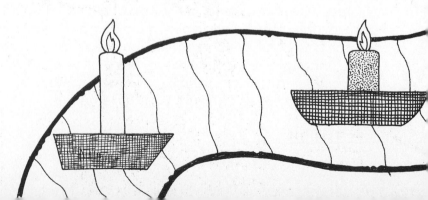

Floating lights

Stage 1

Objectives
One-to-one
correspondence;
comparisons.

What you need
Large sheets of
    paper,
small sheets of
    coloured paper,
candles of all shapes
    and sizes,
paste,
crayons or paints.

What to do
Another activity to celebrate Diwali involves the making of a wall frieze, by as many children as possible. It will show candles floating in divas (small boats) on the sacred River Ganges. The frieze, showing the river, is made up from the large sheets of paper. Each child then chooses a candle from the collection and draws round it on to the frieze. The trace made in this fashion is then coloured in. Each child then makes a small model boat of paper, which is pasted to the frieze so that it seems to support the candle. A pictorial representation can be made of the different coloured divas, to show which colour has been the most or the least popular.

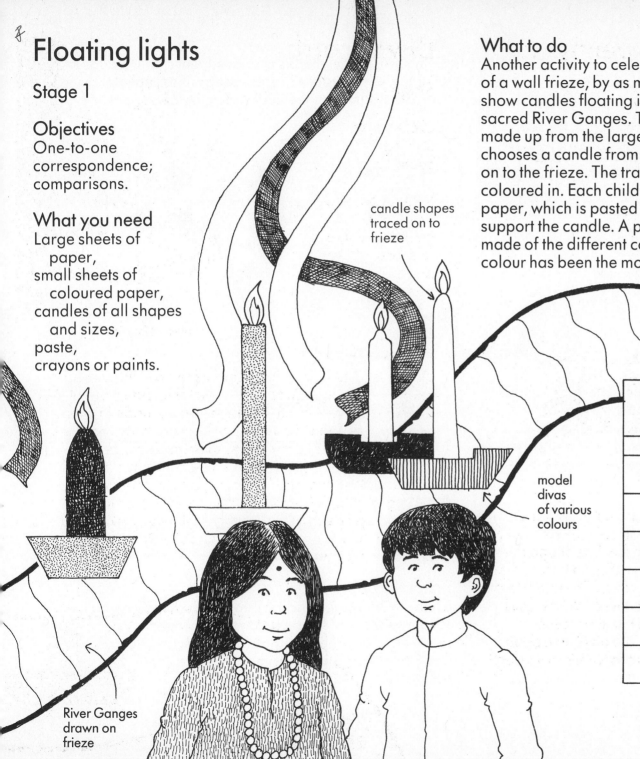

candle shapes
traced on to
frieze

model
divas
of various
colours

River Ganges
drawn on
frieze

Which coloured boat was the most popular?			
Red	Blue	Green	Yellow
⌣	⌣	⌣	⌣
⌣	⌣	⌣	
⌣	⌣	⌣	
⌣	⌣	⌣	
		⌣	

Christmas carols

Stage 2

Objectives
Different ways of
displaying data;
timing.

What you need
Paper,
large sheet of graph
   paper,
timer,
tape recorder.

What to do
The class can hear a selection of Christmas carols or
other songs. Two children can find out the order of
preference of the whole class. The class then splits into
small groups, in order to devise as many different ways
as possible of showing this information. Examples
include many-to-one mapping, block graphs, bar line
graphs and 3-D representations.

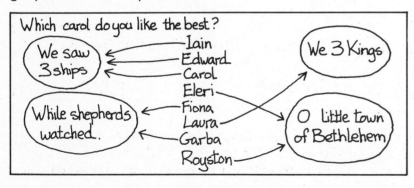

Follow-up 1
Using one of the graphs prepared, get small groups of
children to consider different songs, then make a
Carroll diagram of the kind shown below.

1st choice : We saw 3 ships		
	1st choice	not first choice
girls	Card	Eleri, Fiona, Laura
not girls	Iain, Edward	Garba, Royston

Follow-up 2
Children, working in pairs, can take turns in singing their
favourite song and tape recording it. Then they write
down how long they estimate it took to sing – playing
back the recording and using a timer to check their own
estimates.

Eggs for all

Objectives
Balancing; sorting; counting.

What you need
At least two 250 g packs of ready-made marzipan, icing sugar, cocoa powder, cochineal.

What to do
As an end-of-term treat for the whole class, give each pair of children about 50 g marzipan to make into small Easter eggs. Each 50 g will make about 16 eggs. As it is made, each egg should be balanced against a predetermined 'standard' egg in order to ensure some uniformity. Some of the eggs may then be rolled in icing sugar, some in cocoa powder, some coloured with cochineal and some left plain. Before taking the eggs home or eating them in school, each child should record the number of eggs in the different colours that he and his partner made.

Follow-up

Objective
Towards ideas of ratio.

An extra task might be to find the approximate ratio of chocolate eggs made by the whole class to the number of other eggs:

> ◯ – We made 160 eggs altogether.
>
> ◯ – Chocolate – 70 eggs (less than half 160)
>
> ◯ – Icing sugar – 40 eggs ($\frac{1}{4}$ of 160)

Different ways of recording, however unorthodox, should be devised by the children. The class should discuss which method they find the easiest to understand.

45

Candle lengths

Stage 2

Objective
Linear measurement.

What you need
Paper,
candles,
pencils,
scissors.

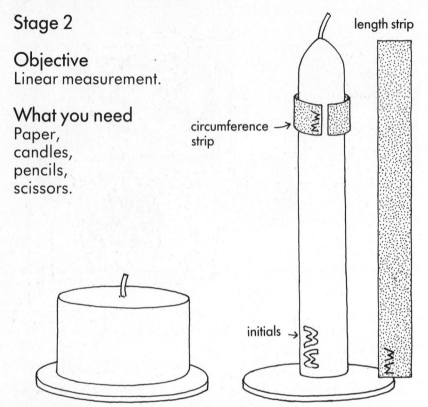

What to do
At Diwali, Christmas or Candlemas (2 February) each child brings in a candle and scratches her initials on the bottom (this saves argument later!). She then cuts a strip of paper the length of her candle, and another strip of paper for its circumference. The length strips are marked with the child's initials and sorted into order; the circumference strips are placed underneath them. Discussion can then follow: Does the longest candle have the greatest circumference? Is the thinnest candle the shortest?

Spring flowers

Stage 2

Objectives
Symmetry;
grouping.

What you need
Paper,
pins,
crayons,
pencils,
scissors.

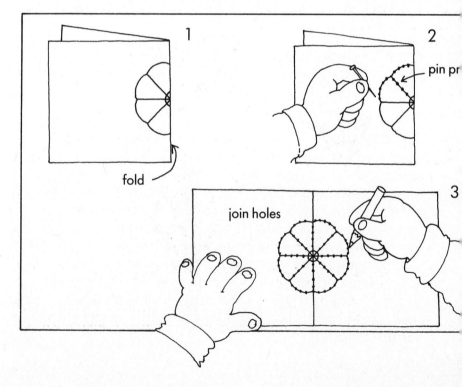

46

What to do

Paper flowers may be made for May Day or for a carnival; you could make daffodils for St David's Day or roses for St George's Day. A sheet of paper is folded in half and petal shapes are drawn on one side up to the fold (1). The child then pricks through the folded paper with a pin at intervals along the outline of the drawn shape (2). The paper is then opened out and the pin pricks joined up with a pencil, so forming the other half of the petal (3). A stem is drawn in and the flower coloured.

The flowers may then be cut out and used to decorate the room, bunched into twos or threes. The number of bunches should be counted and recorded. They could be bunched according to colour or type of flower. Let the children decide the criterion, but make sure that some calculations are done, based around the total number of flowers.

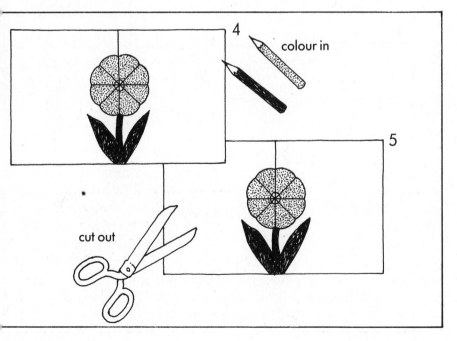

4 colour in

5

cut out

Moon calendars

Stage 3

Objective
Practice in computation.

What you need
A diary or calendar showing festivals and phases of the moon – for this year, last year and next year.

APRIL 19

What to do

Not all festivals are on the same day every year. Easter, for example, is held on the Sunday after the first full moon to occur on or after 21 March. The children can research this and then discuss it in class. Can they find any other religious festivals which vary each year? Working individually or in pairs they can then look up and record the date of Easter Sunday last year, this year and next year.

The children can then work out the number of days between Easter Sunday and Whitsun. Is it the same every year? Is the period between Easter and the Spring Bank Holiday the same every year? Some children might work out the average number of days between Easter Sunday and the Spring Bank Holiday over the three years.

Best buys

Stage 3

Objective
Calculating costs (with or without calculators).

What you need
Pencils,
paper,
calculators
(optional).

What to do
Leading to an end-of-term treat, let the children visit local shops and find out the prices of various popular brands of Easter egg, and their respective weights. Groups can then compile and compare lists of 'best buys this Easter' using calculators if available, or else pencil and paper to work them out. By collecting a small amount from each member of class each week, (commencing about a month before the end of term), money could be spent on the recommended 'best buys' to share out.

Candle time

Stage 3

Objective
Timing.

What you need
At least 2 candles
    of same size and
    thickness,
timer.

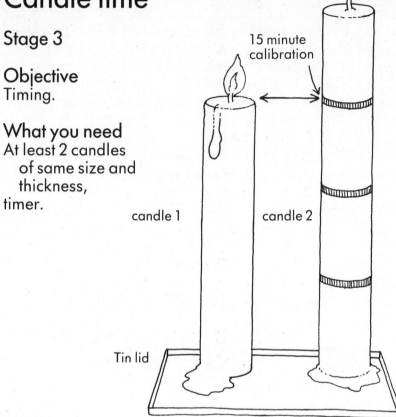

What to do
The teacher lights one candle, firmly fixing it in a tin lid and placing it out of draughts. The timer – an alarm clock or kitchen timer is fine – is set for a quarter of an hour. When it sounds, the height of the burnt candle is marked off on an unlit candle of the same size and thickness. This is continued at 15-minute intervals. The candle marked in this way can be used to calibrate similar-sized candles in quarter-hour intervals. Get the children to estimate how far down each mark will be. This activity can be fitted in with work on Diwali or Christmas, and is suitable either for group or for class work.

Diwali boats

Stage 3

Objectives
Symmetry; floating and sinking.

What you need
Clay,
clay tools,
cake candles.

What to do
The Hindu festival of Diwali celebrates light. On page 43, the children made a frieze of paper candle-boats, or divas. Model divas can be made from clay in the same way as a 'pinch-pot'. Before the model has hardened, a line is drawn around its girth and a symmetrical pattern made on both sides of the line, using a clay tool. When the clay has hardened, it may be coloured and the boat used as a candle holder. The children can experiment with different shapes, and find out which ones will float. The floating divas may be equipped with birthday-cake candles and launched on water.

Note on festivals
Festivals provide ideal opportunities to develop mathematical skills in an enjoyable manner. The objectives pursued in this chapter can be easily adapted to any of the festivals listed below. Which festivals you choose will obviously depend on the nature of the community in which you teach.

The Hindu festival of Raksha Bandhan for example, is a time when brothers and sisters exchange presents. Graphs showing relationships would be a natural follow-up to this festival. Block graphs showing the numbers and kinds of presents would provide numbers for the children to manipulate.

Another much-loved Hindu festival is Holi, during which people throw coloured paint at each other. The modern practice of throwing coloured balloons might be a useful starting point: How many? What colour? Are there more green than red ones?

The Buddhist festival of Vesak celebrates the birth of Gautama Buddha. Food is distributed to the poor, and houses and temples are decorated using flowers and lanterns. In school, making decorations involving patterns and symmetry would be an obvious follow-up.

Spring festivals: St David's Day; St George's Day; St Patrick's Day; Mothering Sunday; Shrove Tuesday; Palm Sunday; Maundy Thursday; Easter; Passover; Holi (March); May Day; Whitsun.
Summer festivals: Father's Day; Midsummer's Day; St Swithin's Day; Eid ul-Fitr (June); Vesak (May/June) Raksha Bandhan (July/August).
Autumn festivals: Harvest festival; Hallowe'en; Guy Fawkes' Night; Martinmas; St Andrew's Day.
Winter festivals: Hanukkah (December); Advent; Shortest Day; Christmas; New Year's Day; Epiphany; Chinese New Year; Candlemas.

DOMINOES
AND CARDS

Sort them out

Stage 1

Objective
Sorting.

What you need
Set of dominoes.

What to do
Remove the double blank domino and give the remaining 27 dominoes to three children to share between them. Each child now takes a turn at sorting his nine dominoes into two sets. His two partners then try to tell him how he has sorted them. Possible groupings might be: all those with or without three dots on them; those that do or do not add up to nine; those with an odd or an even total number of spots.

Each child is given a turn at sorting. If some find this difficult, it might be helpful for you to start off by sorting nine dominoes into two rather obvious sets, and then to question the children as to how the dominoes are grouped. For example:

1 even totals

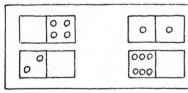

2 odd totals

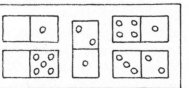

Number stories

Stage 1

Objective
Reinforcing number bonds to 12.

What you need
Set of dominoes, paper, felt-tipped pen.

number line

What to do
Draw up a number line 0 to 12 in bold figures. Working in small groups or individually, let the children pick out any domino and place it on the number line in the appropriate position. For example, a 5,3 domino should go next to the 8. The double 4 domino could be placed next to it. This could lead on to other questions such as: What other numbers belong to 8? Which number on the line has the most dominoes? Can you write the story of 5, using the dominoes?

story of 5

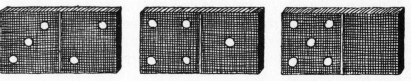

51

Lost dominoes

Stage 1

Objective
Encouraging observation.

What you need
Set of dominoes.

What to do
Lay out all the dominoes face upwards, in any order. Let a small group look at them carefully for a few moments. Choose a child to turn all the dominoes face down, 'shuffle' them, and then remove one. The children turn the dominoes face upwards again, and have to find out which one is missing. To do this, they can arrange them in any way they choose.

Diffy towers

Stage 1

Objectives
Recognition of number symbols; counting; comparisons.

What you need
Pack of playing cards, interlocking cubes.

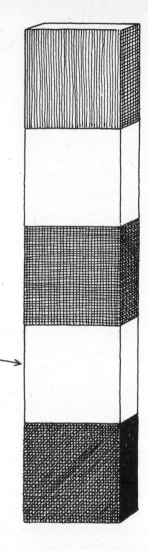

interlocking cubes

What to do
The picture cards are removed from a pack of playing cards. Each player is then asked to pick a card. She counts the number of symbols and builds a tower with that number of cubes. This is repeated twice, and then the towers are compared. Whose tower is the tallest? How many towers are the same height?

Card dominoes

Stage 1

Objective
Practice in ordering numbers.

What you need
Pack of playing cards.

second line

first line

What to do
This is a game of cards for four players. The picture cards are removed from the pack, and the cards dealt equally among the players. The players sort their cards into suits and whoever holds the 7 of clubs plays it face up in the middle of the table. The player on his left must play either a 7 of another suit — which starts a new line — or a 6 or 8 of clubs, to put alongside the 7 of clubs and so continue that line. Play continues in this way. If a player cannot put down a new 7, or continue a line already started, he must miss a turn. The winner is the first player to get rid of all his cards.

How many?

Stage 2

Objective
Computation.

What you need
Set of dominoes, paper, pencils.

What to do
Each pair of children or small group is given a set of dominoes. Put the following questions to them:
How many doubles are there in the set?
How many dominoes have one blank end?
On how many dominoes is the total of dots an odd number?
On how many dominoes is the total of dots an even number?
How many dots are there in the whole set?
The children should record the results as shown above.

Plot-the-dots

Stage 2

Objective
Graphical
representation.

What you need
Set of dominoes,
bag,
graph paper,
pencils.

0	1	2	3	4	5	6	7	8	9	10	11	12

What to do

Place all the dominoes in a bag. A group of children take turns in picking out one domino, counting the total number of dots and plotting that number on graph paper. The domino is then returned to the bag.

The children could be asked to predict the distribution of numbers before they start. After discussion about this, questions might be asked such as: If you threw two dice each time, what would happen? Why?

Dotty dominoes

Stage 2

Objective
Computation.

What you need
Set of dominoes
(for reference).

What to do

Discuss how a normal set of dominoes is made up. It goes up to double 6 and contains 28 pieces going up to double 6. The children can then experiment with other possibilities:

Suppose a set of dominoes only went up to double 1, how many would there be in the set? What kind of pattern would the totals show if they were recorded on graph paper? The children should try this out.

Now they can try a double 2 set . . . or a double 3. Suppose they had a set of dominoes which went as far as double 10. How many dominoes would there be in this set?

What is the total number of dots in each of the sets discussed?

Elevenses

Stage 2

Objective
Reinforcing number bonds.

What you need
Pack of playing cards.

What to do
This is a game for one player. The picture cards are removed from the pack, and the player deals eight cards face up. She looks for pairs of cards which total 11. When she finds a pair, she deals a new card on to each of the pair. She keeps on like this until either she has used all the cards (in which case she has 'won'), or until she cannot go (in which case she 'loses').

Addsnap

Stage 2

Objective
Computation.

What you need
Pack of playing cards.

What to do
This is a game for three or more players. The picture cards should be removed from the pack, and the dealer should shuffle the pack and deal two cards. The first player to call out the *sum* of the two cards wins them. The game is repeated until all the pack has been used. The player with the most cards wins, and becomes dealer for the next round. Scores are kept and totalled after a set number of rounds.

Follow-up
A variation of this game is for the player to call out the numerical difference between the two cards in order to 'win' them. Can the children think of any other variations?

Domino rectangles

Objective
Developing a strategy.

What you need
Sets of dominoes (one for each group).

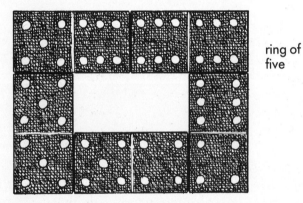

ring of
five

What to do
Show each group of children a rectangle of dominoes, as shown. The five dominoes are matched end to end. Now let each group (or individual) solve the following problems:
Can you make a rectangle of seven dominoes with matching ends?
Now try with eight dominoes, and with eleven.
Now try with all the dominoes in the set. It can be done!

Domino chains

Stage 3

Objective
Numerical
investigations.

What you need
Sets of dominoes (one for each group).

touching halves
make 6

What to do
Make a chain of dominoes as shown, in which the touching halves add up to 6. Then ask the children the following questions:
Can the chain be made to form a closed ring?
What about touching halves which add up to 5? Could they form a closed ring?
A double 6 set will make a closed ring. Will a double 5 set do the same? What about a double 4? Is there a pattern?

Fives and threes

Stage 3

Objective
Practice in addition and division.

What you need
Set of dominoes, cribbage board or pencil and paper.

What to do
A set of dominoes is placed face down on the table. The pieces are shared out equally amongst the players, who may then look at them. The player with double 6 starts the game by laying this domino face upwards in the middle of the table. Each player in turn must then lay down a domino to match one end of the dominoes already on the table, thus forming a chain. Double dominoes are placed crossways. If the combined total of dots at the two ends of the chain is divisible by 5 or 3, the division is carried out: the resulting answer is the score credited to that player. For example, a total of 6 is divided by 3 to give a score of 2.

If the ends add up to a number divisible by both 5 *and* 3 (eg 15) then that player scores 8 points (5 plus 3). Keep the score using a cribbage board or pencil and paper. If a player cannot match either end, then he forfeits that turn and the next player tries. The first player to use up all his pieces is 'Domino', and so gains an extra 5 points.

A new round can now start. The score is kept going for several rounds until one player reaches 61, 101 or some other predetermined score. That player is the winner of the match. There are many variations of this game and the children might like to make up some of their own — for example, scoring points if the combined total of dots is divisible by 5 only.

Target

Stage 3

Objective
Manipulating numerical symbols.

What you need
Pack of playing cards, pencil and paper.

What to do
This game is for any number of players. Take a pack of playing cards and remove the picture cards. Before play starts, any number between 20 and 100 is chosen as a target. Each player is dealt five cards. From these she has to find a combination which leads to the target figure. Some or all of the cards may be used, and any mathematical symbols she knows may be inserted to make a sum. For example, a target of 28 could be made from the cards 1, 4, 5, 5, 6 as follows: $(5 \times 5) + 4 - 1$.

As soon as a player can make the target, she lays the cards down and explains how. If she is correct, she scores the target number of points (in this case, 28). A player who cannot find such a combination can take another card: if she can now make a target, she scores *half* the number of target points. Any player failing to make the target number from that round scores no points. The cards are then shuffled, a new target number settled upon, and the players dealt a new hand of five cards. Scores are kept, and the first player to reach a predetermined number of points is the winner.

TABLE TIME

Lots of twos

Stage 1

Objective
Sorting into
equivalent sets.

What you need
Shallow sorting trays
    such as cardboard
    box lids with 4 or 5
    partitions in each,
any small objects
    suitable for sorting.

What to do
Prepare sorting trays with four or five partitions.
Collect some small objects for sorting, such as acorns,
pebbles, beads, paper-clips, wax crayons. You will need
at least five different types of objects, with two or three of
each. The children work in pairs or individually and sort
out two items into each compartment.
They can then record:

    5 lots of 2 ——→10 things altogether.

On subsequent days put pieces of paper with a different
number written on them in the bottom of the sorting tray
so that sets of twos, threes, fours and fives may be sorted
and recorded.

Bead patterns

Stage 1

Objective
Repeating number patterns.

What you need
Beads,
thread,
card,
pipe-cleaner (optional).

red card

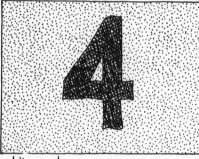

white card

What to do
Prepare sets of white cards, numbered 1 to 10, one set for each player. Then prepare sets of four red cards, numbered either 2, 3, 4 or 5, again with one set for each player. You will also need some cardboard or pieces of pipe-cleaner, to act as 'markers'. Select about 60 large, coloured threading beads.

Children may work individually or in groups. Each child takes a red card (say, 4) which determines the number to be repeated, and then picks up a white card (say, 7) which tells them how many times to repeat the red number. In the example given, the child threads 4 beads 7 times, putting a marker between each lot of 4.

There should be a simple recording (or an oral explanation to the teacher) at the end of each activity. For example:

$$4 \text{ beads } 7 \text{ times} \longrightarrow 28 \text{ altogether.}$$

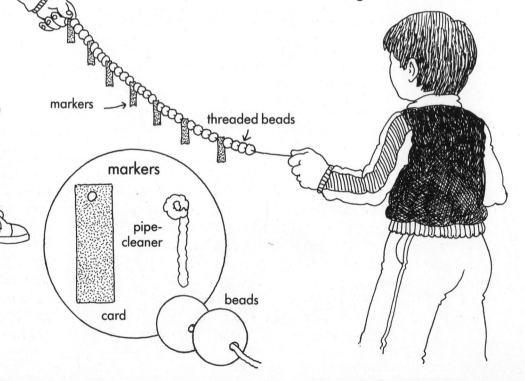

markers →

threaded beads

markers

pipe-cleaner

card

beads

Blockbusters

Stage 1

Objective
Reinforcement of equivalent sets.

What you need
Interlocking cubes, card.

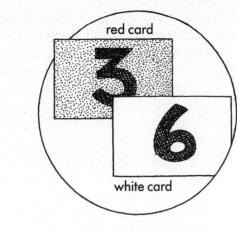

red card

white card

interlocking cubes

What to do
Prepare sets of white cards, numbered 1 to 10, and sets of red cards numbered 1, 2, 3, 4 or 5. The children may work individually or in small groups. Each child picks a red card which determines the number to be repeated, and a white card which shows how many times that number is to be repeated. The child must then build a row of blocks to match the number groups. For example, if a child draws a red 3 and a white 6, he builds 6 towers of 3, and then counts the total number of blocks. The result is recorded:

3 bricks 6 times ⟶ 18 bricks altogether.

Number patterns

Stage 1

Objective
Experiencing number patterns.

What you need
Paper, felt-tipped pens, pencils, coloured crayons.

1	2				
7					12
	14	15			
19	20				
			28		
		33			36

What to do
Using one sheet of paper for each child, draw up a bold 6 × 6 grid about 120 mm square (alternatively, photocopy the grid on page 108). The teacher fills in a few numbers as shown in the figure above. Each child then completes the numbering of the 36 squares in pencil. When this has been done, the child should colour in every second square (2, 4, 6, etc) in red, and discuss the final pattern that emerges. Every third square should then be coloured blue. Is the pattern similar? Are there any numbers coloured over in both blue and red? This activity could then be repeated using a 10 × 10 grid.

Checking pairs

Stage 1

Objective
Counting in twos.

What you need
Interlocking cubes
  of different
   colours,
card,
crayons.

What to do
Prepare pattern cards as shown in Figure 1 below. The children each take a card and then choose cubes to copy the pattern. Discussion follows about the number of 'twos' they have used, and the total number of cubes.

    Figure 2 below shows a more complicated card pattern for the children to follow. Here the paired cubes are of differing colours, thus testing the child's ability to concentrate more closely. It should be emphasised that it is the number of *pairs* that is being counted, and not the number of colours.

Figure 1

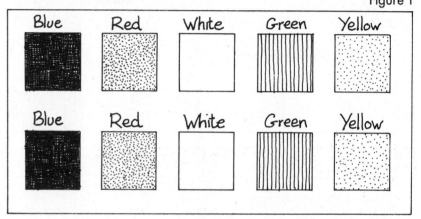

Figure 2

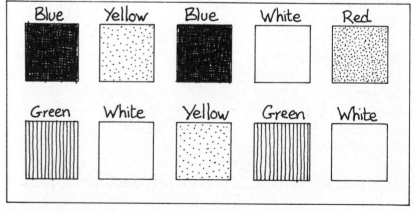

Hurrying home

Stage 2

Objectives
Counting in twos.

What you need
Sheet of strong card,
small cards,
felt-tipped pen,
counters,
die.

What to do
Make a games board as illustrated, marked up boldly, and about 36 small cards marked as shown below (the illustration on page 109 may be photocopied and pasted up). Each player takes turns in 'hurrying home', two steps at a time. He throws a die, and finds the appropriate card from the pile on the table. For example, if a 4 is thrown, then the

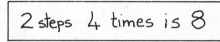

2 steps 4 times is 8

card is found and the counter placed on step 8 on the board. The player records the score and returns the card to the pile; his opponent then takes a turn. The first player to score 24 or more is safely 'HOME'.

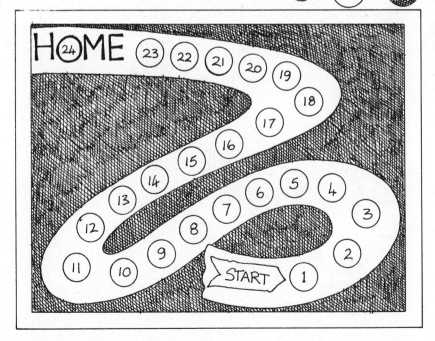

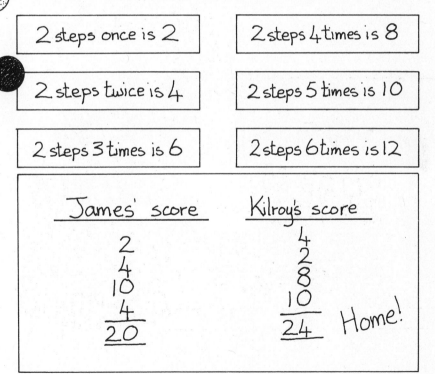

2 steps once is 2	2 steps 4 times is 8
2 steps twice is 4	2 steps 5 times is 10
2 steps 3 times is 6	2 steps 6 times is 12

James' score	Kilroy's score
2	4
4	2
10	8
4	10
20	24 Home!

Halt!

Stage 2

Objective
Repeated
addition.

What you need
Small cubes,
counters,
plastic bag.

What to do
This is a game for two players. One has about ten counters, whilst the other has about 36 small cubes and a plastic bag. The player with the counters starts the game by placing one counter on the table. When she does this the other player responds by putting three cubes in the bag. After five or six goes, the player with the cubes cries 'Halt! How many are in the bag?' Her opponent must then work out, by looking at the counters on the table, how many cubes are in the bag. The number is then checked. If it is correct, the players change places; if not, they start again.

This game can provide a useful check on individual children's understanding of 'repeated addition', especially if the teacher takes the part of the player with the cubes, and is the one to call 'Halt!' at appropriate times.

Who's who?

Stage 2

Objective
Possibilities.

What you need
Card,
pencil.

John	Emma
Hugh	Mark
Smith	Chandler
Steel	Sandra

What to do

Prepare eight cards, five of which show a first name, and three of which show a surname. The children work in pairs, with the cards spread out in front of them. The first player secretly writes down one of the first names and one of the surnames (say John Smith). The second player has to guess the correct combination in as few goes as possible, writing down the final number of guesses he took.

The children then change places and the game continues, the player with the *least* number of guesses being the winner. After playing the game, the players then work out together how many different combinations they can make. In the case of five first names and three surnames the answer is 5×3 (=15). This number fact is then recorded and memorised. The cards can then be used to find and memorise other combinations, such as: 5×2; 4×3; 4×2; 3×3; 3×2; 2×2; 2×1.

Table check

Stage 2

Objective
Practice in multiplication.

What you need
Sheets of card,
felt-tipped pens.

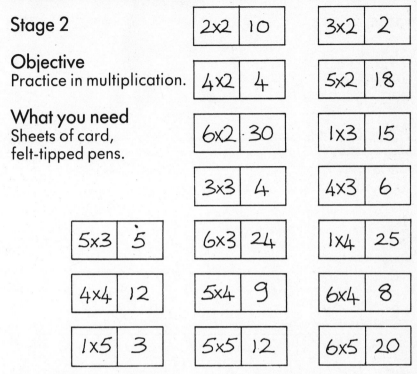

1x2	16
2x2	10
3x2	2
4x2	4
5x2	18
6x2	30
1x3	15
3x3	4
4x3	6
5x3	5
6x3	24
1x4	25
4x4	12
5x4	9
6x4	8
1x5	3
5x5	12
6x5	20

What to do

Prepare 18 domino-like cards as illustrated, or photocopy the cards on page 111, and spread them out on the table. This game is for two players. Each one takes it in turn to place a card next to another so that the product on one card is matched to the correct number on the other, or vice versa, for example:

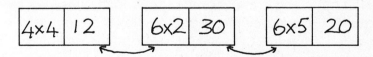

After the completed set has been checked, let the children write down the number facts and memorise them.

Multibingo

Stage 3

Objective
Practice in learning tables.

What you need
Sheets of card, felt-tipped pen.

bingo card

6 × 3		5 × 4
4 × 2	7 × 2	

caller's cards

20

14

18

8

What to do
Prepare bingo cards based on multiplication tables, and a set of matching caller's cards showing the answers (see page 110). The game may be played by three or more players. The caller gives the answer and the first player to recognise the correct multiplication fact on his bingo card claims the caller's card. The winner and subsequent caller is the player to cover all his squares first.

Times square

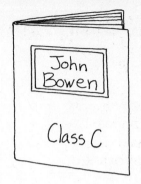

John Bowen

Class C

Stage 3

Objectives
Checking and memorising multiplication facts.

What you need
Paper, pencils.

X	1	2	3	4	5	6	7	8	9	10
1										
2										
3										
4										
5										
6										
7										
8										
9										
10										

What to do
Prepare or photocopy a 10 × 10 grid (see page 113), with a multiplication symbol in the corner. The children fill in their own table square, working in pairs or small groups. They should check with each other to make sure that their facts are correct. These squares are then kept handy, perhaps stuck in books, and used as checks for memorising multiplication facts. As a reinforcement for individual children, the multibingo cards (opposite) may be checked against the square.

Weighing numbers

Stage 3

Objective
The commutative property of multiplication.

What you need
Equaliser balance, washers and hooks, pencils, paper.

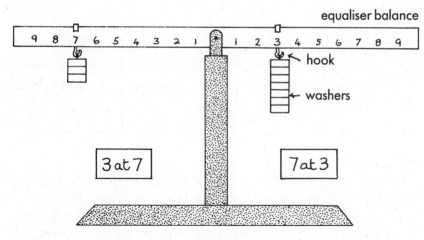

equaliser balance

← hook

← washers

3 at 7

7 at 3

What to do
Working in pairs, children can demonstrate the commutative properties of numbers, and record the results. Washers are hooked to the equaliser balance in relative positions, as shown in the illustration.

Halve the facts

Stage 3

Objective
Minimising number facts to be learned.

What you need
Paper, pencils, ruler.

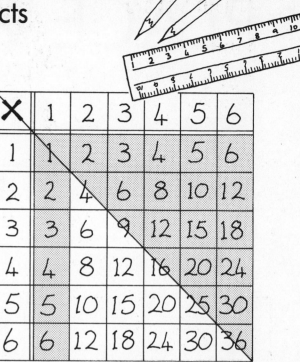

✗	1	2	3	4	5	6
1	1	2	3	4	5	6
2	2	4	6	8	10	12
3	3	6	9	12	15	18
4	4	8	12	16	20	24
5	5	10	15	20	25	30
6	6	12	18	24	30	36

What to do
Prepare or photocopy a large 6 × 6 grid as illustrated, to be used for demonstrating this activity. A small 6 × 6 grid can be drawn by each child in their books, for personal use. On the demonstration square, a diagonal is drawn as shown (once the numbers have been investigated by the class and learnt separately). The 'one times' table can be taken as known; because of the symmetry about the diagonal, only ten further 'facts' remain to be learned.

This activity can be extended to the 10 × 10 square. The children can investigate how many 'facts' now have to be memorised.

Learning multiplication facts should be a gradual process, and the children from time to time can start with a blank 10 × 10 square and see how many entries they can make without having to stop to think.

PLACE VALUE

Rings and overs

Objectives
Counting and grouping.

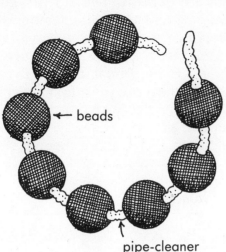

← beads

pipe-cleaner

What you need
Popett beads (if
    available) or
    small beads
    which will thread
    on to a pipe-
    cleaner,
2 dice.

What to do
This is a game for two players. The beads are placed in
the 'kitty', and each child takes it in turn to throw the two
dice. The number of dots are counted and that number of
beads taken from the kitty. The object is to make as many
rings as possible, each ring consisting of eight beads.
If the total is more than eight, the spares are left over
in front of the player until the next turn, when they go
towards making the next ring. After three or four goes
(the rules must be agreed beforehand), the results are
recorded by the players.

number of rings	number of overs	altogether
3	3	27

Through discussions and practice, children will begin
to understand that, for example, '3 rings with 3 over' does
not equal 6, and that 3 on the left-hand side of the above
record is worth more than the other 3.

Filling the boxes

Stage 1

Objectives
Counting and grouping.

What you need
Beads or marbles,
6-hole egg-boxes,
2 dice.

What to do
This is a game for two players which works on the same
principles as 'Rings and overs', only using a different
grouping number. By throwing the dice two (or three)
times, each egg-box can be filled with six beads or
marbles. The players must see how many 'six-boxes' they
can get, with how many 'overs'. After an agreed number
of goes, the results should be recorded, as in 'Rings and
overs'. Sometimes there will be no overs, thus introducing
zero in a meaningful way as a 'place-holder'.

Matchmakers

Stage 1

Objective
Grouping in fives.

What you need
Matchsticks,
small rubber
    bands,
matchboxes,
2 dice,
pencil,
paper.

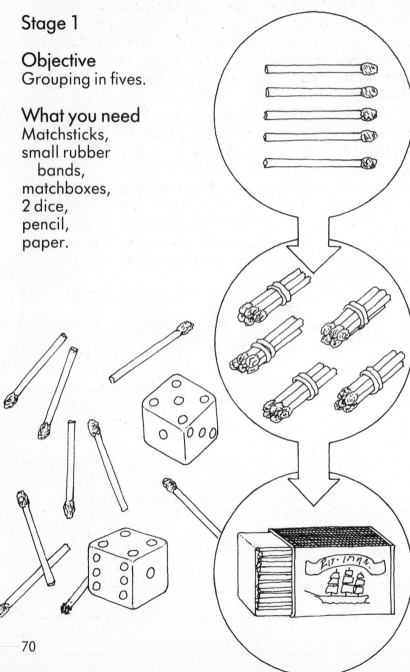

What to do
This is a game for two players. Each player in turn throws two dice and takes that number of dead matchsticks. For every five matchsticks won in this way, a rubber band is needed to make a 'bundle of five'. The 'overs' are left for inclusion in the final total. Every five bundles (25 matches) are put into a matchbox. The winner is the player who fills the most matchboxes over an agreed number of turns. The players record the boxes, bundles and 'overs' on a score sheet as shown:

Name: Ian		bundles of 5	overs
1st go	6 and 2 → 8	1	3
2nd go	5 and 6 → 11	2	1
3rd go	3 and 1 → 4	0	4
	altogether	4	3
altogether 4 bundles and 3 overs → 23 matchsticks			

Name: Ahmed		bundles of 5	overs
1st go	6 and 5 → 11	2	1
2nd go	4 and 6 → 10	2	0
3rd go	5 and 3 → 8	1	3
	altogether	5	4
altogether 1 box, 0 bundles, 4 overs → 29 matchsticks			

Lotto

Stage 2

Objective
Practice in the teen numbers.

What you need
Sheet of card, pencils.

What to do
This is a game for four players. Make three lotto cards as shown below (or photocopy page 112), and 15 caller's cards *written out* as follows: 'one ten and three' (three cards); 'one ten and four' (two cards); 'one ten and five' (two cards); 'one ten and six' (two cards); 'one ten and seven' (two cards); 'one ten and eight' (two cards); 'one ten and nine' (two cards).

Lotto is played in the usual way, the caller reading out her cards, for example, 'one ten and six'. The player must recognise that this means 16 on his lotto card. He claims the caller's card to cover his number. The first lotto card to have all the numbers covered brings that game to an end, but each child should take a turn at being caller irrespective of whether they have won or not. This will ensure that each gets a chance to speak the 'longhand' of the teen numbers as well as recognising the 'shorthand' form on the lotto card.

13			17
16		18	19

14		16	19
	15	13	

14		15	13
17			18

Cover the numbers

Stage 2

Objective
Practice in place value.

What you need
Sheets of card, felt-tipped pens.

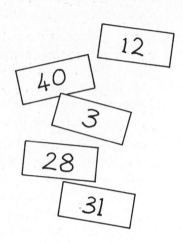

What to do
This can be an individual activity, or it can be played in pairs with an element of speed – the 'winner' being the first to finish. Prepare one or two number boards as shown, with the numbers 1 to 50 written in words, and two sets of cards on which the numbers 1 to 50 are written in figures (see page 114). Each child is given a number board and a set of cards. At the word 'Go!' the words on the board must be covered with the correct numbers. Discussion between teacher and child will lead to observation of patterns and relationships between the numbers. The 'ten more' principle should be emphasised.

one	two	three	four	five
six	seven	eight	nine	ten
eleven	twelve	thirteen	fourteen	fifteen
sixteen	seventeen	eighteen	nineteen	twenty
twenty-one	twenty-two	twenty-three	twenty-four	twenty-f
twenty-six	twenty-seven	twenty-eight	twenty-nine	thirty
thirty-one	thirty-two	thirty-three	thirty-four	thirty-five
thirty-six	thirty-seven	thirty-eight	thirty-nine	forty
forty-one	forty-two	forty-three	forty-four	forty-five
forty-six	forty-seven	forty-eight	forty-nine	fifty

Follow-up
If any child seems to need reinforcement of these skills, a number board of 1 to 100, written out in words, and a set of 1 to 100 number cards can be prepared (see page 115). The work on the 100-board could also be linked with work on a number line. The child starts at any number, jumps forwards or backwards in tens, and then checks with the number board.

High snap

Stage 3

Objective
Recognition of three-digit numbers.

What you need
Sheet of card, felt-tipped pens.

What to do
Prepare packs of about 20 cards, each of which shows a three-digit number. These should include a few with zero in the 'tens' position, and a few with zero in the 'units' position. Also prepare a few duplicate cards (you might like to photocopy the material on page 116).

    The children work in pairs with two packs of cards face down between them. They take turns in turning over the top card and calling out its number to their opponent. If correct, the player keeps that card and her opponent takes a turn. If the wrong number is called out, the card is forfeited to the opponent. If two duplicate cards are turned up consecutively, the player who is the first to call out 'Snap! Three hundred and five!' (or whatever the number happens to be) wins *all* the cards already played. Play continues until all the cards have been used up; the player with the most cards wins.

Order, order!

Stage 3

Objective
Ordering numbers.

What you need
Sheets of card,
felt-tipped pens.

Order! Order!

What to do
Prepare a grid, with ten spaces, for each player, and a set of small cards numbered 0 to 100 which will fit into the spaces on the grid, as shown below. Put the small cards into a bag.

Each player takes turns at drawing a number from the bag, without looking. He must decide in which space on his grid to place the numbers in turn, so that the lowest number is at the bottom and the highest at the top. Once numbers have been placed on the grid, they must *not* be moved, so if a player picks a number which will only fit into a space which is already occupied, he must put it on one side. The winner is the player who gets as many of the numbers as possible, in order, on the grid.

The illustration below shows the grids of three players. Karen got seven numbers on her grid, and is the winner. James was unlucky to lose. He chose sensible places for his numbers but got a lot of low ones and then picked 100 as well as 99. This is a game of both luck and skill.

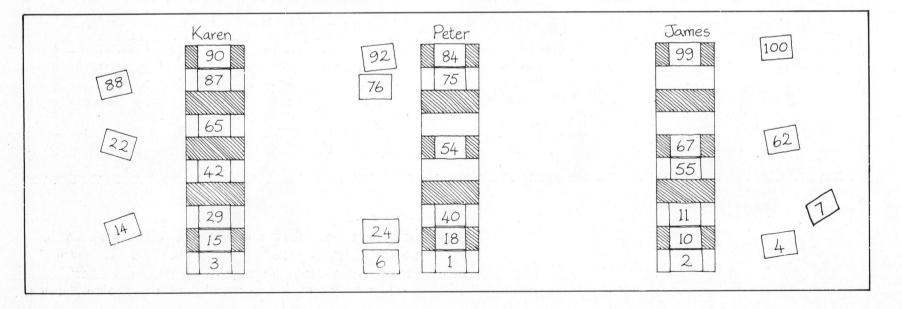

Making the most of it

Stage 3

Objective
Practice in place value.

What you need
Sheets of card,
felt-tipped pens.

What to do
Get the children to make themselves grids as shown below, each with four spaces (photocopies may be taken from page 117). Each space, left to right, represents thousands, hundreds, tens and units. A set of cards numbered 0 to 9 should also be made, making sure that they fit in the spaces on the board.

The game is for two players. Each takes turns at drawing one of the numbers from a bag. As soon as the number is drawn, the player decides where it will be put on the grid. Once the number has been placed on the grid it cannot be moved. The winner is the player who makes the *highest* number after four draws each.

The illustration below shows that David has won even though he got mostly low numbers. Martin picked up the 9, but it was his last number and he only had the units column left – so it didn't help him very much.

Martin				David			
thousands	hundreds	tens	units	thousands	hundreds	tens	units
7	6	5	9	8	3	1	0

Follow-up
One variation of the game could be called 'Making the least of it'. Encourage the children to make up similar games – one to find the player with the highest *odd* number, for example – but don't forget to change the title.

GAMES

Thingamibobs

Stage 1

Objective
Matching shapes.

What you need
Sheet of card,
die.

What to do
Prepare boards as shown (or photocopy page 118), featuring a square, a rectangle, a rhombus, a circle, a triangle and a semicircle, for each player. Cut out lots of shapes from the card to cover the shapes on the board, and paste the same sequence of shapes to the faces of a die.

   Thingamibob is a game for four players or more. The loose shapes (thingamibobs) are placed in a central box. Players take it in turns to throw the die. Depending on the shape that comes up, they must pick a thingamibob of the same shape and position it correctly on their own board, calling out the name of the shape as they do so. The first to present a card that is completely covered is the winner.

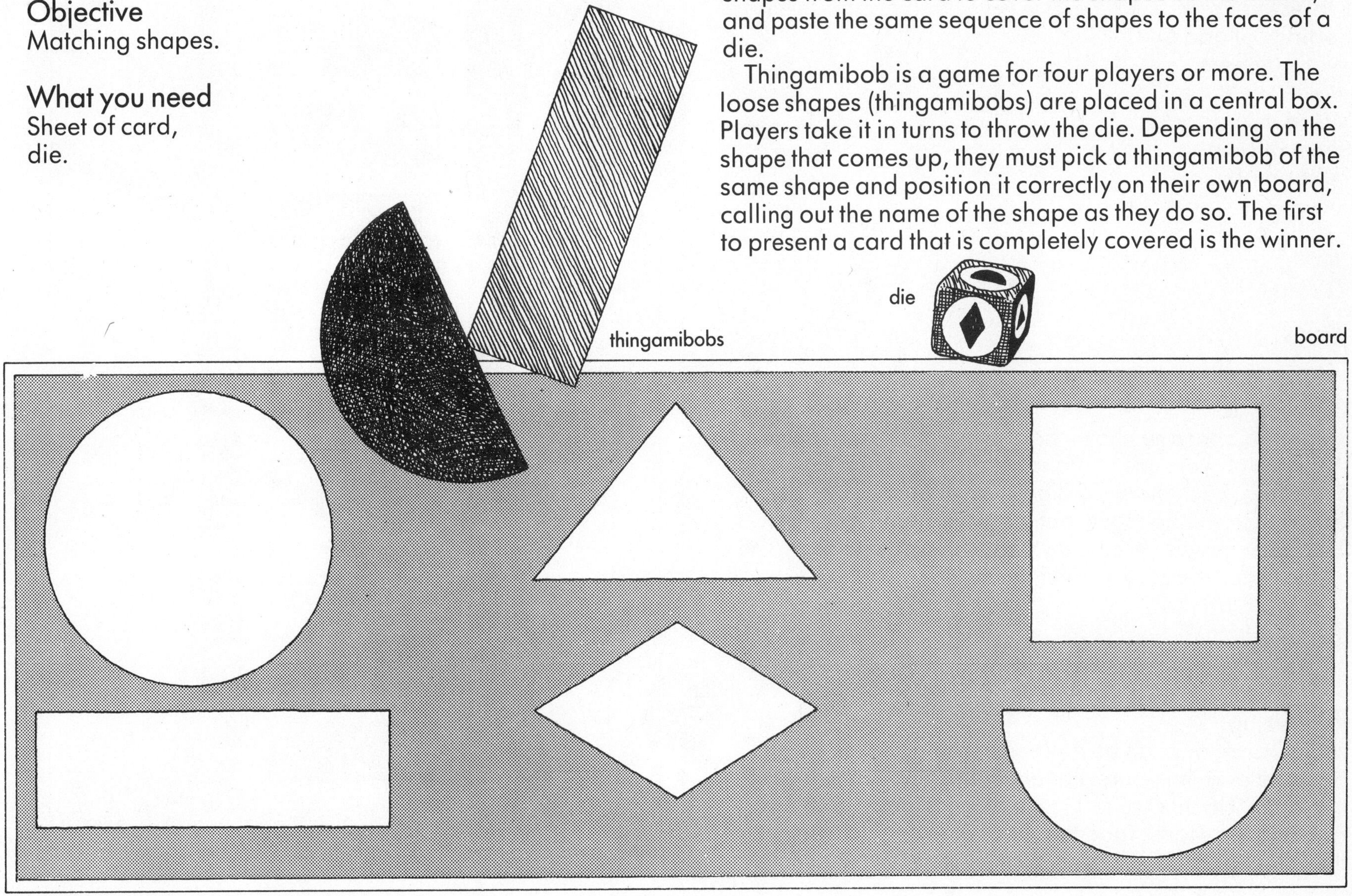

thingamibobs

die

board

Puss in the tree

Stage 1

Objective
Sorting out odd and
even numbers.

What you need
Sheet of card,
felt-tipped pen,
dice,
counters.

What to do
Prepare a board as shown or photocopy the one on page
119. Two players are trying to rescue the cat from the top
of the tree. Each throws a die in turn. If an *odd* number is
thrown, there is no move, but if an *even* number is thrown,
the player moves his counter one rung up the ladder. The
first to reach the cat is the winner.

Follow-up
Many variations can be devised to reinforce the idea of
odd and even numbers. For example, you might have
two dice, 0 to 5 and 6 to 11; the players throw both dice
and add the scores together. They then decide whether
their answer is odd or even and whether they can move.

Clearing the attic

Stage 1

Objective
Counting on and back.

What you need
Sheets of card, felt-tipped pens, counters.

What to do
Prepare a board as shown in the illustration or photocopy the one one page 120. You will need about 20 cards with instructions such as 'go up 3' or 'fall down 2'. You will also need six small cards with pictures of books, bricks, etc, to represent the 'parcels' in the attic. There are three players. Each one chooses a ladder and starts with his counter halfway up the ladder (see START). The players have to 'bring down' their two parcels one at a time. They do this by picking the card which will tell them to go up or fall down by a given number of rungs. The first player to bring down both parcels wins.

Sally   Josie   Jim

START   START   START

Number people 1

Stage 1

Objective
Place value (tens and units).

What you need
Sheet of card, felt-tipped pen.

What to do
This game involves the whole class. Divide the children into equal teams, with no more than ten in each. A caller and each team hold an identical set of cards, each one about 10 cm × 15 cm, and numbered 0 to 9 for a team of ten, 0 to 5 for a team of six, and so on. Within a team, each child holds a different number card.

The caller shouts out any number with two digits, provided each digit is different, for example: 94 but not 88 for a team of ten, 43 but not 44 for a team of five. It must of course be possible to make the number called from the cards issued. As soon as the number is called, the first team to send out 'number people' to face the class with the numbers in the correct order scores a point. The game is repeated, and the score recorded over a predetermined number of goes. The team with the highest score is the winner.

Follow-up
Many variations of this game are possible. Simple addition sums might be called, with the 'number people' coming out to form the answer with their cards.

What's the difference?

Objective
Numerical
difference.

What you need
2 dice,
counters,
sheet of card,
felt-tipped pen,
or a Snakes and
    Ladders board.

What to do
Prepare a 100-square grid on a sheet of card, or use
a Snakes and Ladders board. Each player throws two
dice and records the score, then throws the dice again
and records the second score. She then works out the
difference between the two scores, and this represents
the number of squares she may move. For example: if the
first throw is 6 and 1 (total 7) and the second throw is 5
and 3 (total 8), the difference between the two totals is 1,
and the player moves one place. Other players then take
turns, and the first to reach 100 is the winner. Variations
are many; for example, the difference might be
doubled.

Hoopla!

Stage 2

Objective
Halving,
doubling and
adding.

What you need
6 cardboard
    tubes,
thin card,
scissors,
sticky tape,
paints.

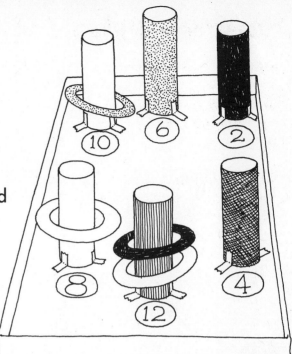

What to do
Collect six cardboard tubes or make cylinders from thin
card. Paint each one a different colour and stick them in a
shallow box lid with an even-numbered score beside
each. Each player needs at least three rings to play with.
These can be made by sticking together two cardboard
circles whose centres have been removed. Make sure
that the rings are large enough to fit over the cylinders,
but not so large that they knock against the others.
Colour the rings the same colours as the cylinders.
   The children take turns at throwing their three rings and
scoring. If a ring lands over a cylinder of the same colour,
the score is halved. The winner is the child with the
highest score after an agreed number of turns. The
children should be able to think of variations on this
game – doubling instead of halving, for example.

Shunting about

Objective
Developing a
strategy.

What you need
Counters,
card.

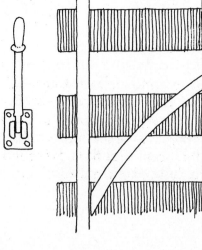

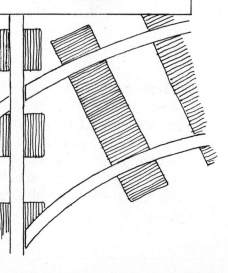

What to do
Prepare a board from card as shown or photocopy the
illustration on page 121. This is a game for two players.
One places four counters of one colour on the top row,
the other places four of another colour on the bottom
row. Each player has to change over the positions of his
set of counters. Counters can slide to an empty space in
any direction except diagonally. They can't jump over
each other, and they can't share a space. The winner is
the first player to get his four counters to the opposite
row.

Times snap

Stage 2

Objective
Multiplication practice.

What you need
Pack of playing cards.

6 × 3

What to do
After removing the jack, queen and king of each suit, the dealer shows the first two cards from the pack. The first player to call out their correct product picks up the two cards. The player who has the most cards when the pack is used up becomes the dealer for the next round. The children will be able to think of variations of this game.

Number people 2

Stage 2

Objective
Place value (hundreds, tens and units).

What you need
Sheet of card, felt-tipped pen.

What to do
This is a more advanced version of the game played on page 80. Divide the class into equal teams, with no more than ten in each. The caller and the teams each have an identical set of cards (approximately 10 cm × 15 cm) numbered 0 to 9 for a group of ten, 0 to 5 for a group of six, and so on. The caller shouts out any number with three different digits: 'Nine hundred and sixty!', for example. For a group of ten, this will of course have to be not more than 987, and for a group of six the number will have to be not more than 543. The first team to send the correct 'number people' in front of the class, with their numbers in the right order, scores a point. The game is repeated, points are recorded and results determined after a specified number of calls. Many variations of this game are possible: one suitable for this stage would be to call out 'What is the number two more than 199?'

Meeting place

Stage 3

Objective
Developing a strategy.

What you need
Card,
counters.

What to do
Prepare a 25-square grid and number it as shown. The blue player places her counter on any blue arrow and the red player places hers on any red arrow. The blue counter is then moved downwards until it meets the red counter, which is being moved across. The number where the two paths intersect is the red score. For example, blue puts a counter on the fourth column, red puts a counter on the fifth row. The intersection is at 4 across and 5 down. This is 9, which is red's score. Next, red starts first, and the game continues with alternate starts. The scores are recorded and the total arrived at after a predetermined number of moves. (The grid may be photocopied from the illustration on page 122.)

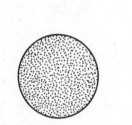

RED \ BLUE ↓	↓	↓	↓	↓
→	1	6	2	9	4
→	7	3	4	1	4
→	5	1	10	3	2
→	2	4	9	1	7
→	3	8	1	9	0

It's a goal!

Stage 3

Objective
Developing a
strategy.

What you need
Card,
felt-tipped pen,
coin.

KICK OFF	1	2	3	4	5	6	7	8	9	10
	11	12	13	14	15	16	17	18	19	20
	GOAL	22	23	24	25	26	27	28	29	30
	31	32	33	34	35	GOAL	37	38	39	40
	41	42	43	44	45	46	47	48	GOAL	50
	51	52	53	54	55	56	57	58	59	60
	61	GOAL	63	64	65	66	67	68	69	70
	71	72	73	74	75	76	77	78	79	80
	81	82	83	GOAL	85	86	87	88	89	90
	91	92	93	94	95	96	97	98	99	GOAL
										FULL TIME

What to do
Draw up a 100-square grid as shown and cut out a
football from card to fit in the squares (alternatively,
photocopy the grid shown on page 123). Toss a coin to
see who kicks off. The first player moves as many squares
as he likes up to ten. The second player then takes over
the ball and also moves any number of squares up to ten.
A goal is scored each time a ball lands on a goal square.
Players keep a record of the scores. The winner is the
player with the most goals after an agreed number of
games.

'football' counter —
cut to fit
over squares

Trains

Stage 3

Objective
Developing a strategy.

What you need
Card,
crayons,
felt-tipped pen,
counters,
die.

What to do
Prepare a board as illustrated, or photocopy the illustration on page 124, and colour in the 'stations' as shown. You will also require four counters in these same colours, and a die on which the faces have been pasted over with the figures 0, 0, 0, 1, 1, 1. The four counters represent trains, and the aim of the game is to get the trains to their correct stations in as few moves as possible.

Players each choose a colour, throw a die in turn and move the counters down the lines. 0 means 'go left', and 1 means 'go right'. There will be times when the player will have to decide whether to move or remain where he is until he throws a more favourable number.

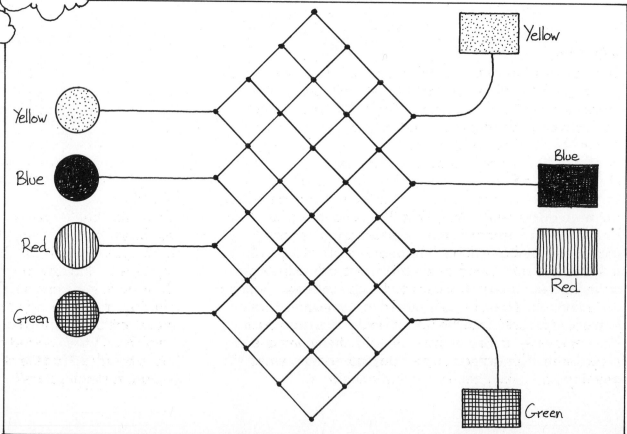

Number people 3

Stage 3

Objective
Place value (thousands, hundreds, tens and units).

What you need
Card, felt-tipped pen.

What to do
Simpler versions of this game are to be found on page 80 and page 83. Divide the class into equal teams, with no more than ten children in each. The caller and the team each have an identical set of cards (approximately 10 cm × 15 cm) on which there are written different numbers, one for each player. For a group of ten, these should be 0 to 9; for a group of six, 0 to 5, and so on.

The teacher acts as caller and calls out a number made up of four different digits: 'One thousand, three hundred and forty-two!', for example. (For a team of ten the maximum number will be 9,876; for a team of six it will be 5,432.) The first team to assemble four cards in the right order scores a point. A joker card for each team might be included, which can be substituted for any single digit. The game is repeated, the points being recorded each time. After a specified number of calls, the winning team is declared. This game can be adapted in many ways, to develop other skills such as multiplication.

Mighty magic squares

Stage 3

Objective
Manipulation of numbers.

What you need
Felt-tipped pen, card or paper.

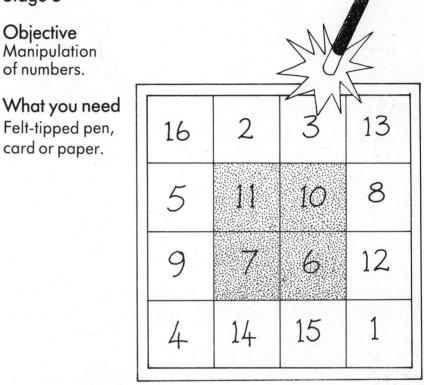

What to do
The child should draw up a 16-square grid and number it as shown (to save time, photocopies of the grid may be taken from page 125). The numbers 1 to 16 fit into the squares so that any row across, down or diagonally, adds up to the same number. Working individually, the children should first find out that number. How many more sets of numbers can they find that add up to the same total? The shaded area offers a clue, but there are more besides. Can the children make up a mighty magic square for themselves?

PUZZLE IT OUT

O'Grady says . . .

Stage 1

Objective
Meaning of *not*.

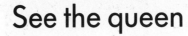

What to do
At first you take the role of 'O'Grady', although this may be transferred to any of the children when they catch on to the aim of the game. Instructions are given, such as 'O'Grady says do this . . . do this . . . do *not* do this'. The children must listen for the *not* command extra carefully, and are 'out' if they continue the activity mentioned.

See the queen

Stage 1

Objective
Sorting, counting and comparisons.

What you need
Pack of playing cards.

What to do
Take the picture cards from the pack and spread them out on the table. Working in small groups or as individuals, get the children to sort out how many queens there are, and how many 'not queens'. The two groups are sorted, counted and compared. This can be repeated with 'not kings' and 'not jacks'.

What-nots

Stage 1

Objective
Sorting into just
two sets.

What you need
An assortment
of toys.

What to do
Get a group of children to sort out some 'nots' of their
own, choosing from a set of toys. A starter might be to
sort out toys which are red and those which are not red.
If they find this confusing, try some simple sorting
yourself, and let them try to tell you what the 'nots' are.
They can also try this exercise on each other.

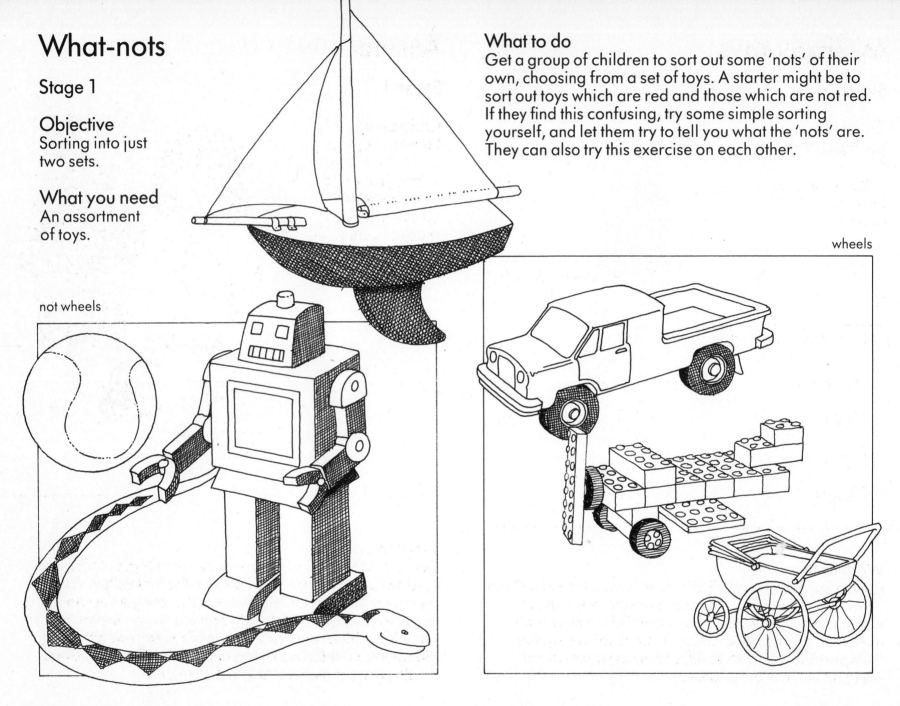

wheels

not wheels

Missing 'm's

Stage 1

Objective
Sorting sounds.

What you need
Pencils,
paper.

These names have 'm'	These names do not have 'm'
Miriam	Jenny
Mike	Lisa
Thomas	Rakeesh
Moira	Paul
	Kulwinder
	Rosie
	Susan

What to do
From a list of children's first names, let each child call out his or her name if it does *not* contain the letter 'm', for instance (the letters may be varied). This activity is also useful for phonic work. Lists may be made, or signed 'self-portraits' by each child, of names which do *not* contain the letter in question.

Allsorts

Stage 1

Objective
Sorting shapes.

What you need
2 sets of logic blocks or similar shapes in coloured card.

What to do
Give a small group of children one set of logic blocks or card shapes. They must sort out first the 'not yellows', and then, from that set, the 'not triangles'. Now get the same group to reverse the order of sorting by using the second set of logic blocks or card shapes. They start with the 'not triangles' and then find out from that set the 'not yellows'. Finally, discuss the results with the children.

Shaping up

Stage 2

Objective
Use of Carroll diagrams.

What you need
Logic blocks or
  card and
  scissors,
paper,
pencils.

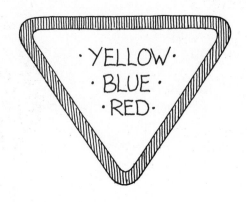

What to do

Spread out a selection of logic blocks of different shapes and colours, or of coloured cards cut to different shapes. Before sorting starts, make it clear that each piece can be described in terms of shape and colour. For instance, if looking for a piece that is both triangular and red, it is necessary first to distinguish between pieces that are red and those that are not red, as well as between pieces that are triangular and those that are not triangular. There is only one piece in the collection which satisfies both criteria, and that is the red triangular piece. Each of the remaining pieces is either not red or not triangular. A convenient way of sorting the pieces is to use a Carroll diagram, as illustrated. The children can then arrange the actual pieces in the correct sections.

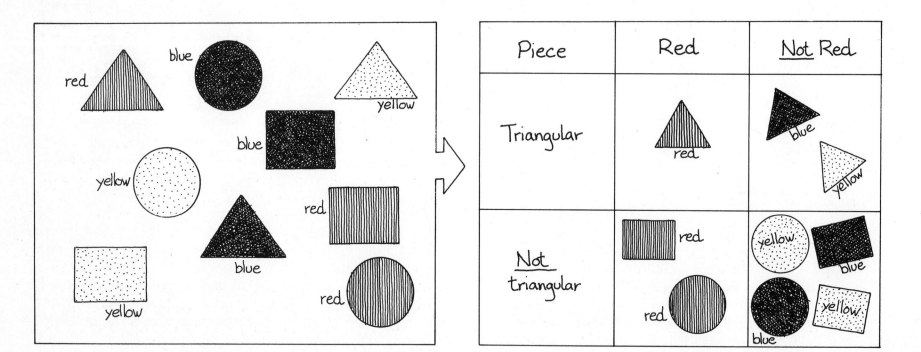

Right or not right?

Stage 2

Objectives
Computation;
meaning of *not*.

What you need
Paper,
pencils.

What to do
Write out a list of sums as illustrated (but geared to individual levels of ability). Children are asked to put a ring around the sums that are *not* right.

(2 + 2 = 5)	not right
3 + 3 = 6	right
(1 + 1 = 3)	not right
(5+5 = 9)	not right
(2+1 = 4)	not right
7+2 = 9	right

Sort yourselves out

Stage 2

Objective
Collecting and displaying information.

What you need
Paper,
pencils.

	boys	not boys
stay to dinner	Henry, Simon Garba	Wendy, Sita, Tayo, Anna.
not stay to dinner	Ashley, Siva, Ben Kenny, William	Zoe, Angharad, Ellie.

What to do
Using the whole class as a 'set', groups can gather information which is divisible into positive and negative statements. For example, those who do and those who do not stay to lunch *and* which are boys and which are not (ie girls). The results can be recorded in a Carroll diagram as shown.

Follow-up
Working in small groups, and choosing their own criteria, children could go on to make other Carroll diagrams, for example, having brothers/*not* having brothers, having sisters/*not* having sisters.

Tell the truth

Stage 3

Objectives
Sorting; truth tables.

What you need
Logic blocks or card and scissors.

What to do
For this activity, nine coloured shapes are required, as illustrated on page 92. These can be logic blocks or they can be simply cut out from coloured card. Discussion preceding the activity should emphasise that for any statement which is held to be true, the corresponding negated statement must be held to be false, and vice versa. This might seem to be obvious, but it is nevertheless, well worth pointing out. After such a discussion, the children could draw up a 'truth table', using the shapes:

piece	red	not red	△	not △
red △	true	false	true	false
red ●	true	false	false	true
blue ▲	false	true	true	false
blue ●	false	true	false	true

Follow-up
Some children might now be ready to consider combinations of statements and to make a truth table for the logic statement: 'It is both red and triangular'.

piece	red	△	both red and △
red △	true	true	true
red ●	true	false	false
blue ▲	false	true	false
blue ●	false	false	false

Either . . . or . . .

Stage 3

Objective
Logic.

What you need
Logic blocks or
   card and scissors.

What to do
This activity is similar to the one shown on the opposite page, but it goes further by using both a 'truth table' and a Carroll diagram. You will need two sets of logic blocks or the card shapes illustrated on page 92. Working in groups, the children should choose a shape not used in previous activities, such as a blue circle. The group then decide where all the pieces fit in on the truth table:

piece	blue	◯	either blue or ◯
● blue	true	true	true
▭ yellow	false	false	false
◯ yellow	false	true	true
◉ red	false	true	true
▥ red	false	false	false
◭ red	false	false	false
△ yellow	false	false	false
▲ blue	true	false	true
▰ blue	true	false	true

Another group then fills in the Carroll diagram, using the second set of shapes:

piece	blue	not blue
◯	● blue	◯ yellow ◉ red
not ◯	▲ blue ▰ blue	▥ red △ yellow ▭ yellow ◭ red

The groups might then notice that the top-left entry in the Carroll diagram is the same as the shape which has all three attributes rated 'true' in the truth table. They might also notice that the 'true' entries in the third column of the truth table (either blue or circle) correspond with the entries in the Carroll diagram, with the exception of the bottom right-hand entries (neither blue nor circle).

Punch cards

Stage 3

Objective
Collecting and storing information.

What you need
Punch cards or
  sheets of card and
  scissors,
pencils,
dowelling or
  knitting-needles.

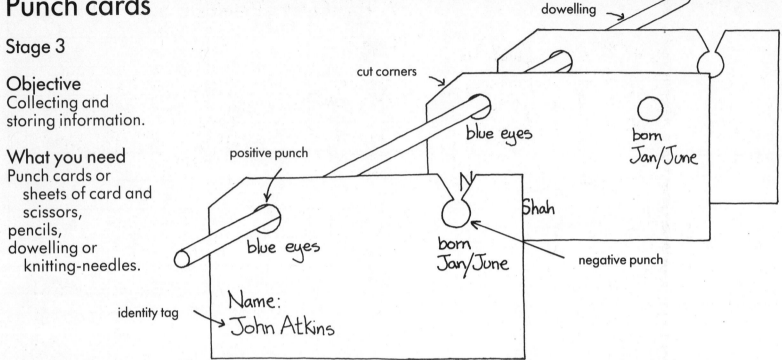

dowelling

cut corners

blue eyes

born
Jan/June

positive punch

blue eyes

Shah

born
Jan/June

negative punch

identity tag

Name:
John Atkins

What to do
Punch cards may be purchased or made in class. If children make their own, they must ensure that the holes of all the cards are similarly positioned, with a corner cut to show the right way round.

There are many variations of the 'true/false' exercises described on the previous pages which make use of truth tables or Carroll diagrams. The same concept can be profitably transferred to other situations. A punch card, for example, might be used to indicate whether the child in question is blue-eyed, and in which half of the year he was born. Each child puts his or her name on the card and specifies the two attributes being recorded. The hole is left intact for the positive, and cut to form a slot for the negative. In the illustration above, for example, the card

tells us that John has blue eyes, but was not born between January and June.

To collate the information from the class, all the punch cards are lined up and a thin dowel or knitting-needle inserted through one hole (say, 'blue eyes') and lifted. The 'not blue' cards, will fall away, leaving behind 'blue eyes' cards on the dowel. The dowel can then be inserted in these remaining 'blue eyes' cards to find those who are *both* blue-eyed *and* born in the first half of the year.

Children should then be encouraged to gather information of their own choice – sports, pets, etc, and store it for future retrieval, whether as punch cards or as the Carroll diagrams and truth tables already discussed.

Square eyes

Stage 3

Objective
Investigating
shapes.

What you need
Paper,
pencil.

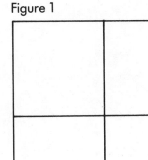

Figure 1

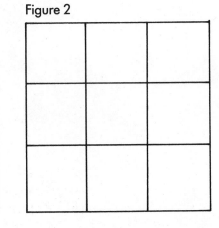

Figure 2

What to do
The children should draw up a 2 × 2 square as shown in
Figure 1. Ask them how many squares they can see.
(There are of course, five). Then get them to experiment
with a 3 × 3 square (Figure 2); a 4 × 4 square and so on.
Results should be recorded.

Matchstick puzzle

Stage 3

Objective
Making shapes.

What you need
20 matchsticks
(at least).

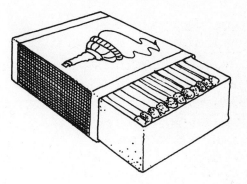

What to do
Show a child this pattern of five squares made from
twelve dead matchsticks. Then ask him to find out how
many squares he can make using 20 matchsticks. No
cheating is allowed! Matches must not be broken or bent,
and must meet only end-to-end.

Cows and bulls

Stage 3

Objective
Educated guessing.

What you need
Pencil,
paper.

What to do
This is a game for two players. One player thinks of a four-digit number and writes it down, not letting her opponent see it. The opponent starts to guess the number and the first player tells her how many 'cows' she has, and how many 'bulls': a 'cow' is a correct number, whilst a 'bull' is a correct number in the *right place*. If, for example, the number thought of is 4,729, and the first guess is 1,234, the response would be '2 cows' because the 2 and the 4 are correct but in the wrong place. The guesser writes down her guesses, noting that she has two 'cows' before trying again. The winner is the player who guesses a number in the least number of times. This will be recognised as an early version of the popular strategy game, Mastermind.

Thirty-sixers

Stage 3

Objective
Problem-solving.

What you need
Pack of playing cards.

5H	4H	9H	6c	2c	10c
3H	8H	7H	4c	9c	5c
10H	6H	2H	8c	7c	3c
9s	5s	4s	10D	6D	2D
7s	3s	8s	5D	4D	9D
2s	10s	6s	3D	8D	7D

What to do
Remove the aces and picture cards from a pack and give them to one child. The puzzle is to arrange the 36 remaining cards in a 6 × 6 square so that:
1 The total of each row is 36.
2 The total of each column is 36.
3 No two cards of the same number are in the same row, column or diagonal.
4 Each row and column has three red and three black cards.
5 One diagonal is made up of red cards only, and the other of black cards only.

Find the pattern

Stage 3

Objective
Number patterns.

What you need
Pencil,
paper.

What to do
Get the children to try completing some of the following sequences. They should then try making up similar problems for their friends.

(add 4)
□, □ 11, 15 19, 23 □, □, □, 39

(×2)+1
2, 5, 11, □, 47

square numbers
1, 4, 9, □, 25 □

(+3)
3, 6, 9, □, 15, □, □, □, 27

MATERIAL
TO COPY

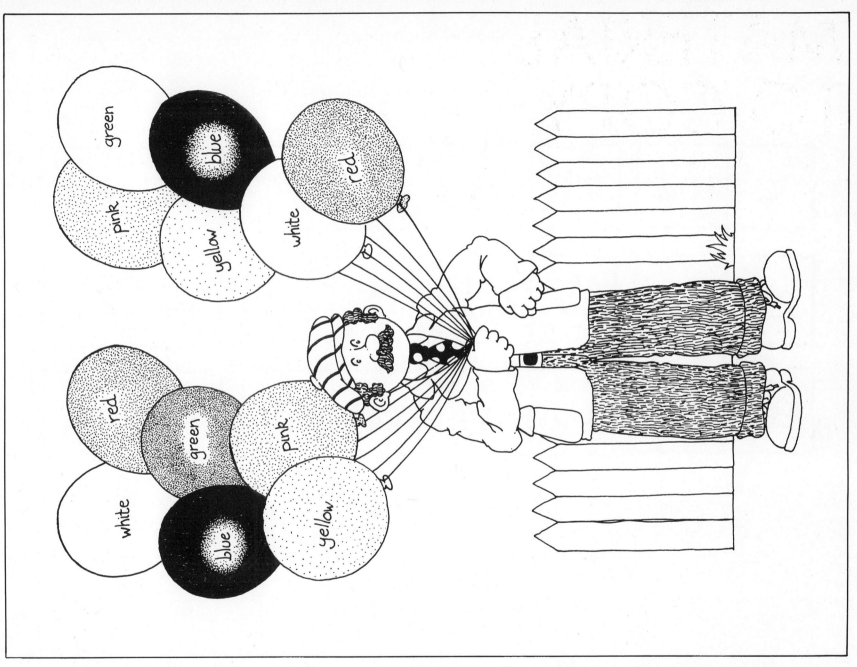

This page may be photocopied for use in the classroom and should not be declared in any return in respect of any photocopying licence.

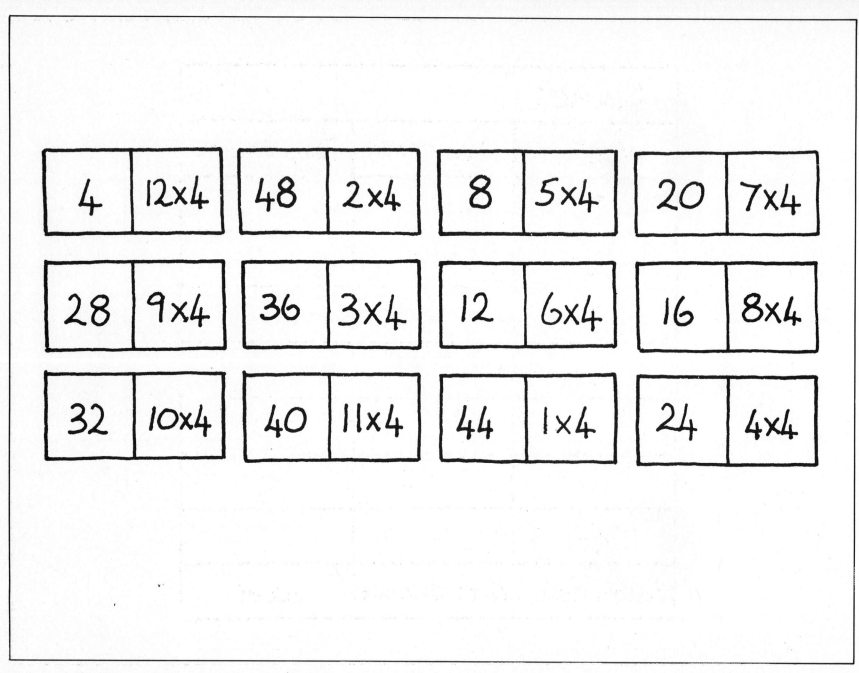

4	12x4	48	2x4	8	5x4	20	7x4
28	9x4	36	3x4	12	6x4	16	8x4
32	10x4	40	11x4	44	1x4	24	4x4

This page may be photocopied for use in the classroom and should not be declared in any return in respect of any photocopying licence.

Name:		
Week.	Days present	Days absent
1		
2		
3		
4		
5		
6		
Total		
No. of weeks with no absence		out of

This page may be photocopied for use in the classroom and should not be declared in any return in respect of any photocopying licence.

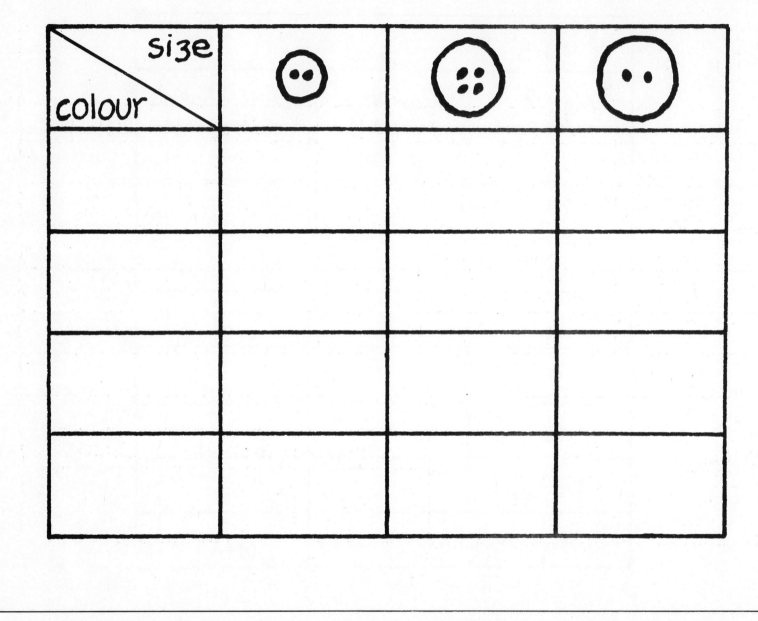

This page may be photocopied for use in the classroom and should not be declared in any return in respect of any photocopying licence.

Name :

Throw	die score	large	medium	small
1				
2				
3				
4				
5				
6				

Name:	Total	large	medium	small

This page may be photocopied for use in the classroom and should not be declared in any return in respect of any photocopying licence.

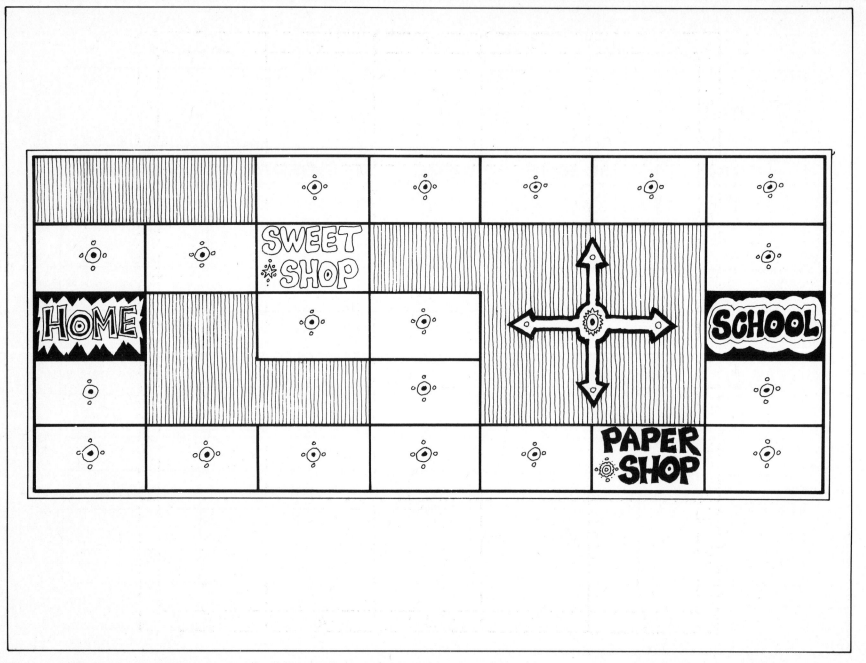

This page may be photocopied for use in the classroom and should not be declared in any return in respect of any photocopying licence.

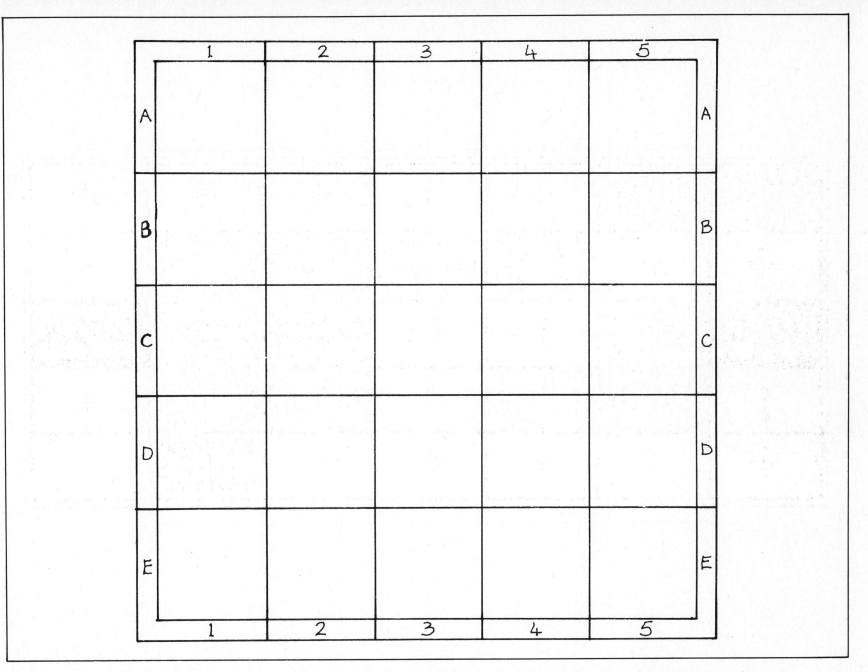

This page may be photocopied for use in the classroom and should not be declared in any return in respect of any photocopying licence.

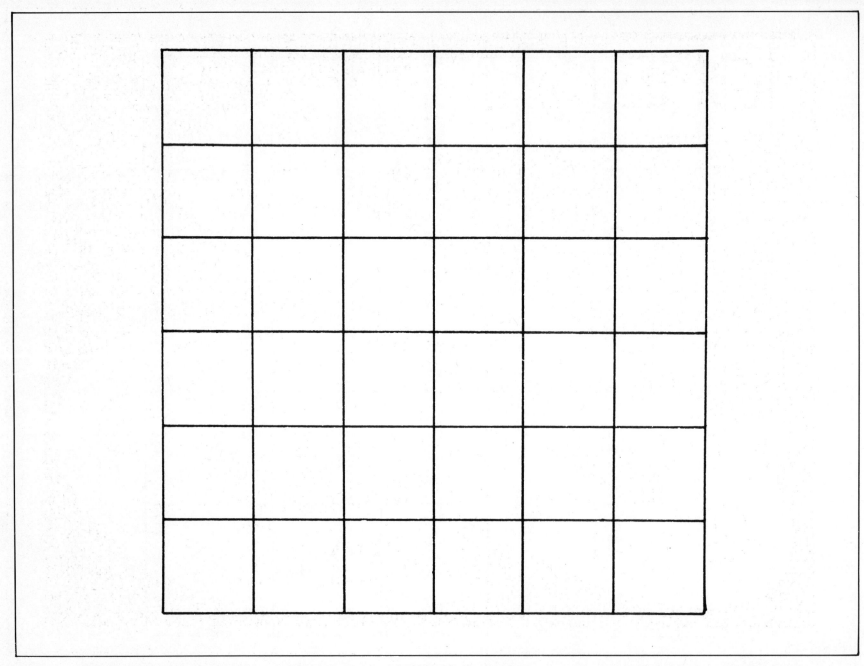

This page may be photocopied for use in the classroom and should not be declared in any return in respect of any photocopying licence.

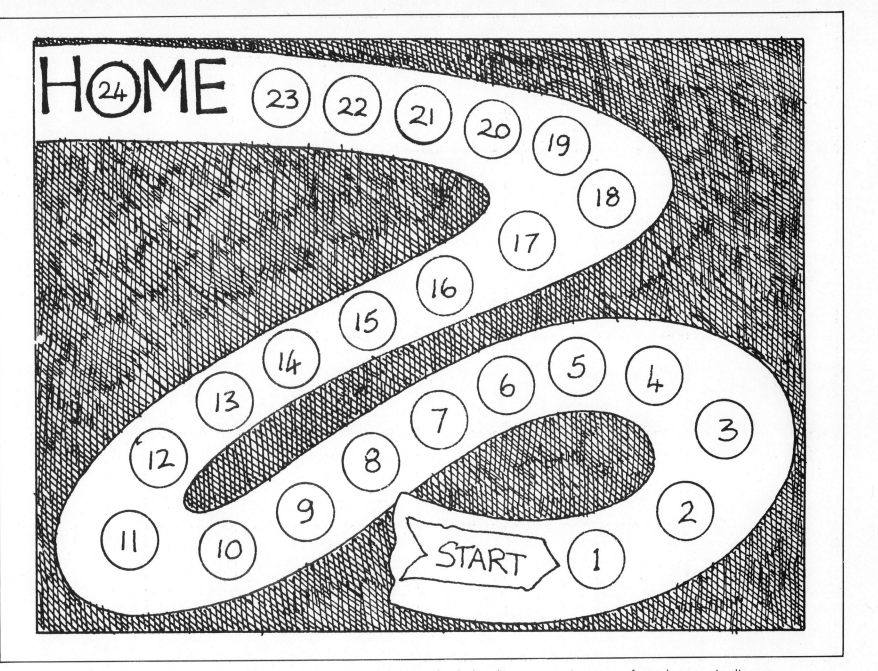

This page may be photocopied for use in the classroom and should not be declared in any return in respect of any photocopying licence.

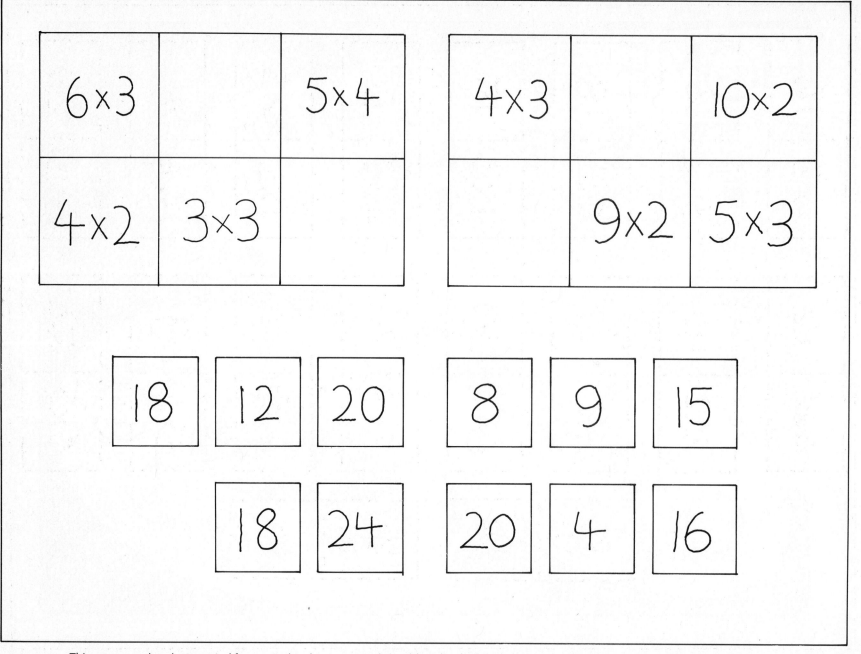

6×3		5×4
4×2	3×3	

4×3		10×2
	9×2	5×3

18	12	20	8	9	15
18	24	20	4	16	

This page may be photocopied for use in the classroom and should not be declared in any return in respect of any photocopying licence.

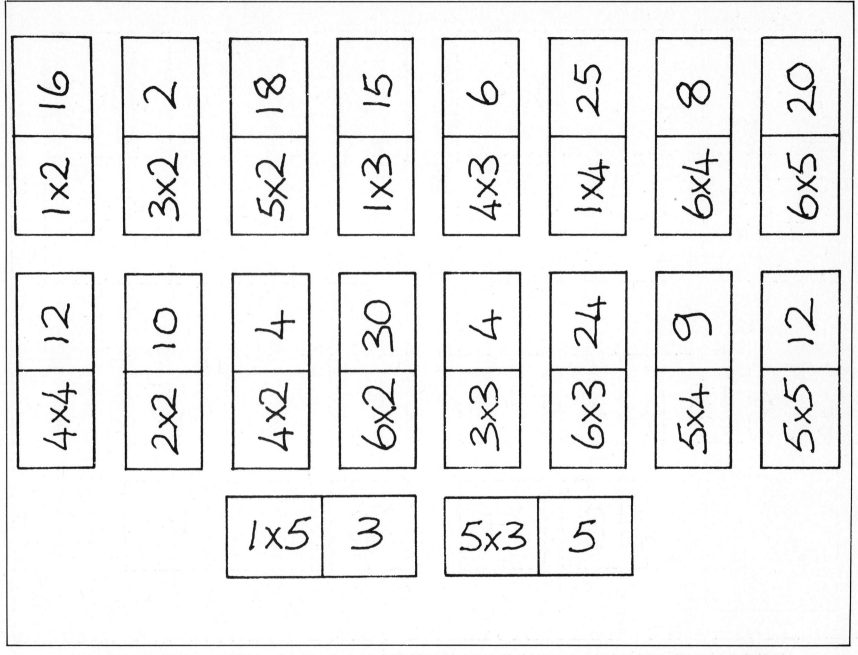

1x2	16	3x2	2	5x2	18	1x3	15
4x3	6	1x4	25	6x4	8	6x5	20
4x4	12	2x2	10	4x2	4	6x2	30
3x3	4	6x3	24	5x4	9	5x5	12

1x5	3

5x3	5

This page may be photocopied for use in the classroom and should not be declared in any return in respect of any photocopying licence.

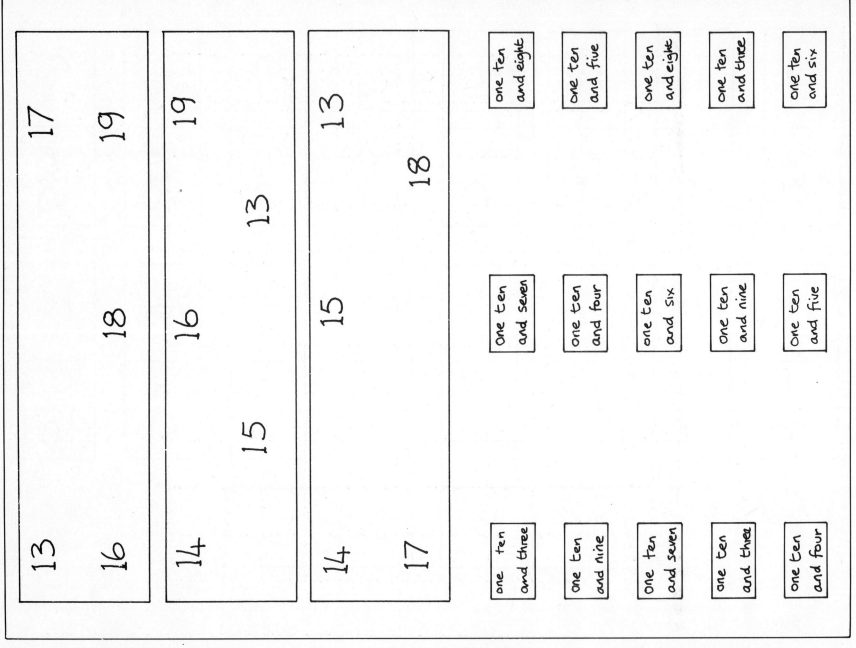

This page may be photocopied for use in the classroom and should not be declared in any return in respect of any photocopying licence.

X	1	2	3	4	5	6	7	8	9	10
1										
2										
3										
4										
5										
6										
7										
8										
9										
10										

This page may be photocopied for use in the classroom and should not be declared in any return in respect of any photocopying licence.

one	two	three	four	five
six	seven	eight	nine	ten
eleven	twelve	thirteen	fourteen	fifteen
sixteen	seventeen	eighteen	nineteen	twenty
twenty-one	twenty-two	twenty-three	twenty-four	twenty-five
twenty-six	twenty-seven	twenty-eight	twenty-nine	thirty
thirty-one	thirty-two	thirty-three	thirty-four	thirty-five
thirty-six	thirty-seven	thirty-eight	thirty-nine	forty
forty-one	forty-two	forty-three	forty-four	forty-five
forty-six	forty-seven	forty-eight	forty-nine	fifty

This page may be photocopied for use in the classroom and should not be declared in any return in respect of any photocopying licence.

one	two	three	four	five	six	seven	eight	nine	ten
eleven	twelve	thirteen	fourteen	fifteen	sixteen	seventeen	eighteen	nineteen	twenty
twenty-one	twenty-two	twenty-three	twenty-four	twenty-five	twenty-six	twenty-seven	twenty-eight	twenty-nine	thirty
thirty-one	thirty-two	thirty-three	thirty-four	thirty-five	thirty-six	thirty-seven	thirty-eight	thirty-nine	forty
forty-one	forty-two	forty-three	forty-four	forty-five	forty-six	forty-seven	forty-eight	forty-nine	fifty
fifty-one	fifty-two	fifty-three	fifty-four	fifty-five	fifty-six	fifty-seven	fifty-eight	fifty-nine	sixty
sixty-one	sixty-two	sixty-three	sixty-four	sixty-five	sixty-six	sixty-seven	sixty-eight	sixty-nine	seventy
seventy-one	seventy-two	seventy-three	seventy-four	seventy-five	seventy-six	seventy-seven	seventy-eight	seventy-nine	eighty
eighty-one	eighty-two	eighty-three	eighty-four	eighty-five	eighty-six	eighty-seven	eighty-eight	eighty-nine	ninety
ninety-one	ninety-two	ninety-three	ninety-four	ninety-five	ninety-six	ninety-seven	ninety-eight	ninety-nine	one hundred

This page may be photocopied for use in the classroom and should not be declared in any return in respect of any photocopying licence.

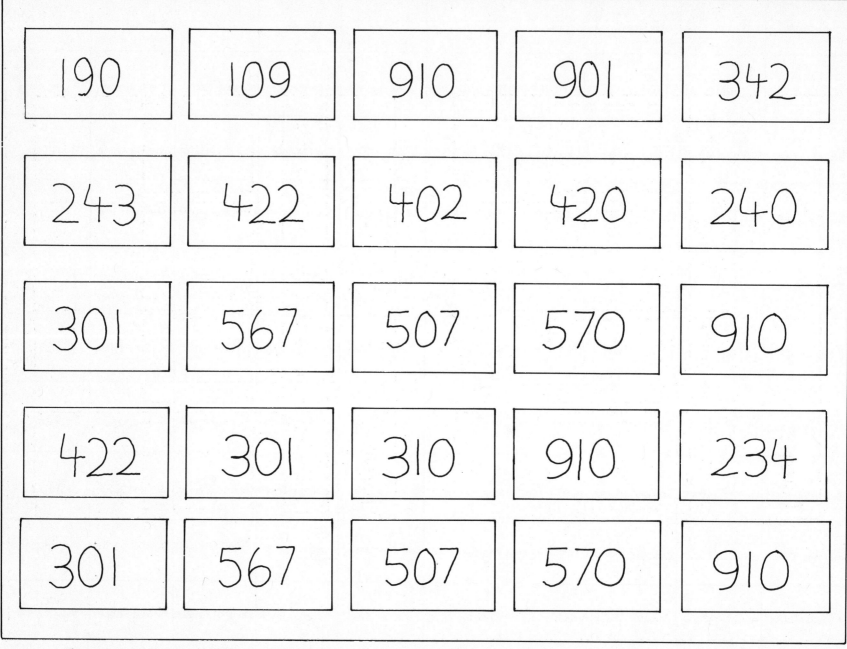

190	109	910	901	342
243	422	402	420	240
301	567	507	570	910
422	301	310	910	234
301	567	507	570	910

This page may be photocopied for use in the classroom and should not be declared in any return in respect of any photocopying licence.

Name	thousands	hundreds	tens	units

Name	thousands	hundreds	tens	units

This page may be photocopied for use in the classroom and should not be declared in any return in respect of any photocopying licence.

This page may be photocopied for use in the classroom and should not be declared in any return in respect of any photocopying licence.

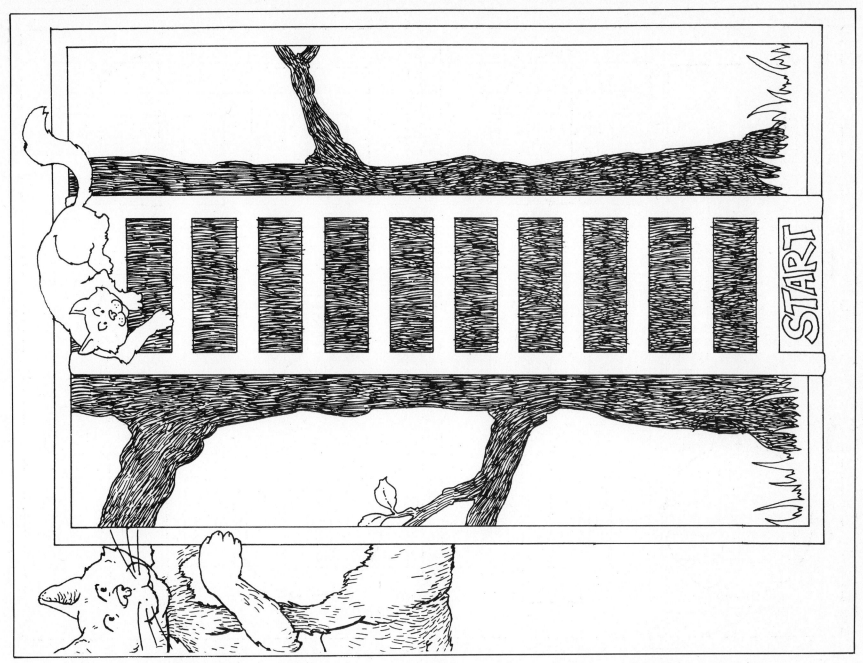

This page may be photocopied for use in the classroom and should not be declared in any return in respect of any photocopying licence.

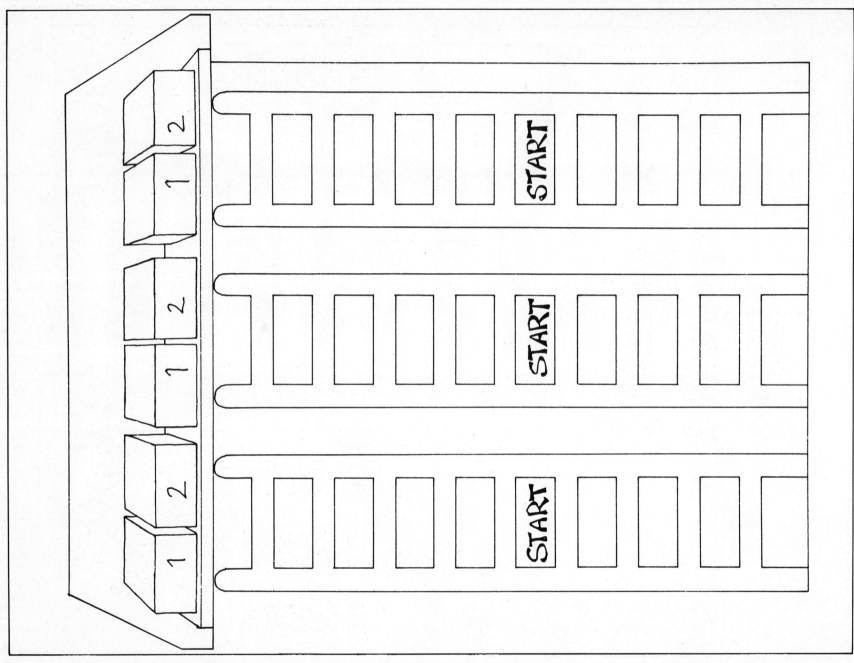

START

START

START

This page may be photocopied for use in the classroom and should not be declared in any return in respect of any photocopying licence.

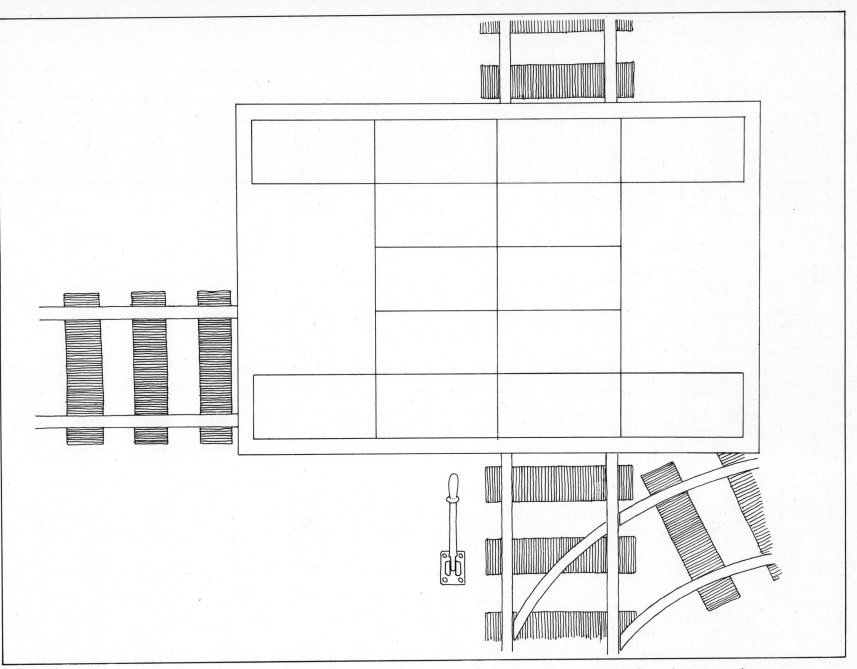

This page may be photocopied for use in the classroom and should not be declared in any return in respect of any photocopying licence.

BLUE RED	↓	↓	↓	↓	↓
→	1	6	2	9	4
→	7	3	4	1	4
→	5	1	10	3	2
→	2	4	9	1	7
→	3	8	1	9	0

This page may be photocopied for use in the classroom and should not be declared in any return in respect of any photocopying licence.

KICK OFF	1	2	3	4	5	6	7	8	9	10
	11	12	13	14	15	16	17	18	19	20
	GOAL	22	23	24	25	26	27	28	29	30
	31	32	33	34	35	GOAL	37	38	39	40
	41	42	43	44	45	46	47	48	GOAL	50
	51	52	53	54	55	56	57	58	59	60
	61	GOAL	63	64	65	66	67	68	69	70
	71	72	73	74	75	76	77	78	79	80
	81	82	83	GOAL	85	86	87	88	89	90
	91	92	93	94	95	96	97	98	99	GOAL
										FULL TIME

This page may be photocopied for use in the classroom and should not be declared in any return in respect of any photocopying licence.

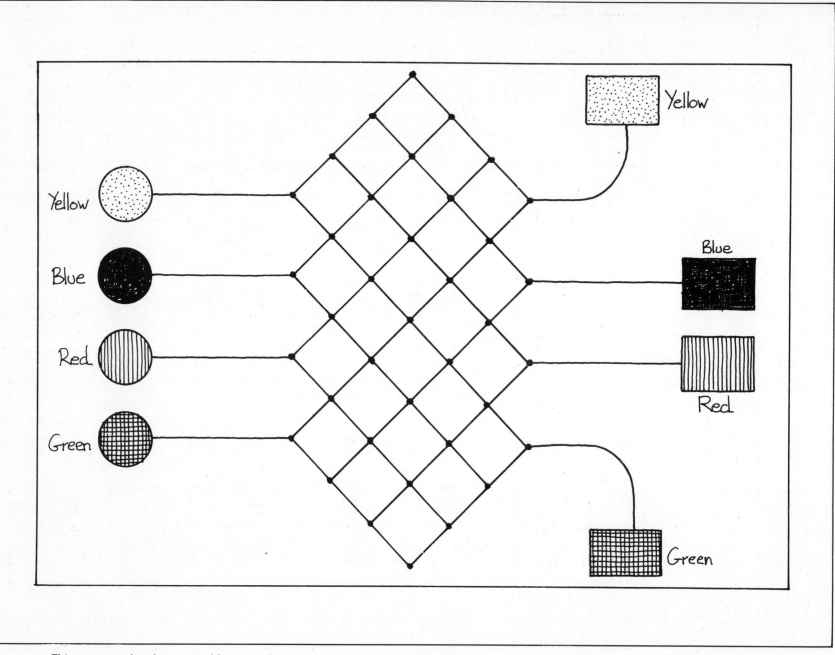

This page may be photocopied for use in the classroom and should not be declared in any return in respect of any photocopying licence.

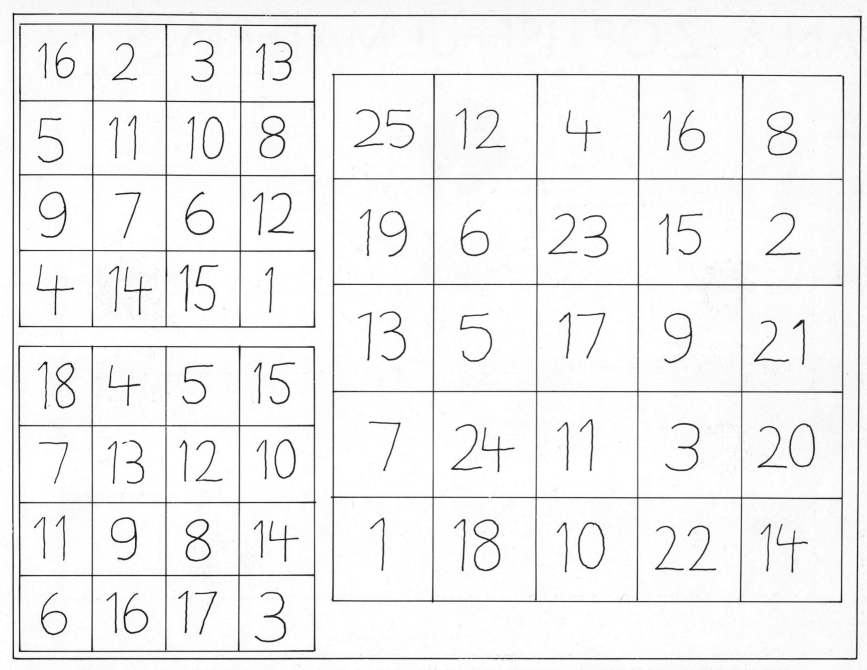

16	2	3	13
5	11	10	8
9	7	6	12
4	14	15	1

18	4	5	15
7	13	12	10
11	9	8	14
6	16	17	3

25	12	4	16	8
19	6	23	15	2
13	5	17	9	21
7	24	11	3	20
1	18	10	22	14

This page may be photocopied for use in the classroom and should not be declared in any return in respect of any photocopying licence.

AN A–Z OF USEFUL MATERIALS

A
abacus
acorns

B
bags
balance
beads
boxes
buttons

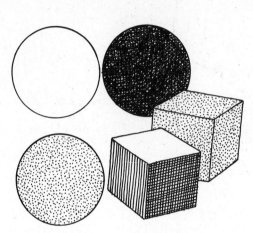

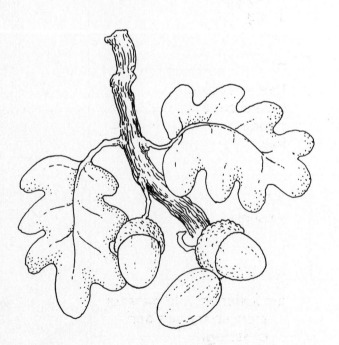

C
calculators
calendar
candles
card (thick and thin)
cardboard tubes
chalk
chenille stems
cocktail sticks
coins
compass
clay
clipboards
clock
counters
cubes (interlocking and others)
cribbage board

D
diary
dice
dominoes
dowelling

E
egg boxes
egg timer
equaliser balance

F
feathers
felt-tipped pens
foil

G
glitter spray
glue
gummed shapes

H
hooks

K
knitting-needles

L
logic blocks

M
magazines
marbles
matchboxes
matchsticks
mirror

N
needles
newspapers
number lines

P
paints
panel pins
paper (sugar, plain, graph,
    gummed and coloured)
paste
pebbles
pins
pipe-cleaners
Plasticine
playing cards
Popett beads
punch cards

R
ribbons (various lengths
    and widths)
rubber bands (some very
    long for sets, some short
    for bundling)
rulers

S
scissors
scrapbooks
shells
sorting trays
spinners
sticky tape
string

T
tape-measure
tape recorder
thread
toys

W
washers

Z
zip fasteners (old ones for
    measuring units and
    ordering)

ACKNOWLEDGEMENTS

The editors and publisher extend grateful thanks for the reuse of material first published in *Junior Education* to: Peter Seabourne for 'Tell the truth'; Don Maxwell for 'Shunting about', 'Meeting place', 'It's a goal' and 'Mighty magic squares'; Alan Parr for 'Elevenses', 'Addsnap', 'Target', 'Times square' and 'Thirty-sixers'; Jan Stanfield for 'Diffy towers', 'Domino rectangles', 'Order, order!' and 'Make the most of it'; William Lythgoe for 'Networks'; William Blades for 'Trains'.

Every effort has been made to trace and acknowledge contributors. If any right has been omitted, the publishers offer their apologies and will rectify this in subsequent editions following notification.